To Red

LOVE (AWKWARDLY)

A full-length comedy by
John Rotondo & Maryann Carolan

Love,
Maryann Carolan

www.youthplays.com
info@youthplays.com
424-703-5315

COPYRIGHT RULES TO REMEMBER

1. To produce this play, you must receive prior written permission from YouthPLAYS and pay the required royalty.

2. You must pay a royalty each time the play is performed in the presence of audience members outside of the cast and crew. Royalties are due whether or not admission is charged, whether or not the play is presented for profit, for charity or for educational purposes, or whether or not anyone associated with the production is being paid.

3. No changes, including cuts or additions, are permitted to the script without written prior permission from YouthPLAYS.

4. Do not copy this book or any part of it without written permission from YouthPLAYS.

5. Credit to the author and YouthPLAYS is required on all programs and other promotional items associated with this play's performance.

When you pay royalties, you are recognizing the hard work that went into creating the play and making a statement that a play is something of value. We think this is important, and we hope that everyone will do the right thing, thus allowing playwrights to generate income and continue to create wonderful new works for the stage.

Have a question about copyright? Please contact us by email at info@youthplays.com or by phone at 424-703-5315. When in doubt, please ask.

CAST OF CHARACTERS

EDDIE -Joe
WENDY - me
RANDY - Josh
CHARLOTTE - Gabe
LAURA - Keyla
GEORGE -
LUKE —
ROXANNE - Jules
NINJAS
VARIOUS STUDENTS
JACK -
JESSICA

SETTING

The stage is empty except for a large screen or blank wall up center. At various points throughout the play, images and video are projected onto the screen or wall.

AUTHORS' NOTE

The character of Wendy requires a special talent—for example, the ability to walk on her hands. References to this in the script should be considered flexible and tailored to the individual actor and production.

ACT I

SCENE 1 — EDDIE & WENDY

EDDIE: My life is complicated. I hate it when my mother tells me "You don't know how good you've got it, Edward! No responsibility, no job, no mortgage. All you have to do is go to school and do some homework and that's it!" That's it? She's kidding, right? Way to minimize my life entirely, Mom. On the surface, I guess she's right — that's how it seems. I have the carefree existence of a child...or small, fuzzy farm animal. Last Easter, my parents bought me and my brother a baby chick. At first it was great. Everyone wanted to touch it and cuddle it — "It's soooo cute! Let me hold it!" Pretty soon my brother had poked the thing half to death. After a week, I had to dodge the chicken poop all over the floor just to get to my room. Two weeks later, all everyone argued about is who had to feed it. In four weeks, that cute, fuzzy yellow chick had turned into this awkward, ugly monster. My dad kicks it surreptitiously as he passes. People shun it. That's me. I'm the ugly chicken. *(He imitates the chicken pathetically:)* No one wants to hold me or be with me now. And when I get older, I'm going to end up alone, being stuffed into the oven for someone's Sunday dinner.

(Wendy bounces in.)

WENDY: Wanna come for dinner Sunday? We're having your favorite!

EDDIE: Roast chicken. *(To Wendy:)* Sure? Six?

WENDY: Uh huh — call me later!

EDDIE: A few months ago we started this thing where I eat dinner with her family. It's nice. Different from my house. No one drinks beer with dinner there. I think her family really likes me.

WENDY: My family thinks he's kinda weird.

EDDIE: I once told her that she's the best friend I've ever had.

WENDY: He once told me that I'm the best friend he's ever had.

EDDIE: I'm an idiot.

WENDY: He's really sweet.

EDDIE: We met freshman year. Around October.

WENDY: It was November of our freshman year.

EDDIE: Some Junior was picking on her in the hall and making rude comments.

WENDY: He was trying to impress some junior girl.

EDDIE: I, you know, stood up to him.

WENDY: He walked right into an open door.

EDDIE: He popped me in the nose.

WENDY: He was popped right in the nose.

EDDIE: Blood was everywhere.

WENDY: There was hardly any blood.

EDDIE: But I think she appreciated it.

WENDY: He ran to the nurse.

EDDIE: She helped me to the nurse.

WENDY: When he got back to Algebra, he had this big wet pink stain all over the front of his white shirt. I felt bad for him. We've been friends ever since.

EDDIE: We've been friends ever since.

WENDY: He's my best friend. I can trust him. Some girls can't have guys as best friends. But somehow, Eddie's not really a guy-guy in my mind. (*Pauses to consider this for a moment:*) Funny, I'm not really..."sure" about him, you know? Anyway, we're best friends.

(*She exits. He stands there for a moment looking at the space she occupied.*)

EDDIE: Yeah. Best friends. She trusts me. I'd never do anything to betray that trust. She's had some...tough times, so I know how important my trust and friendship are. (*Finally getting it:*) She's not "sure" about me? What does that mean? She's not "sure" I'm a guy? That's borderline offensive? I AM a guy! Jesus. (*Looking back at the empty space:*) She doesn't wear perfume, thank God. But whenever she borrows my sweatshirt or hat, I can smell her hair on it for days. God, I want her.

(*Blackout.*)

SCENE 2 — THE COFFEEHOUSE

(*RANDY and CHARLOTTE sit at a small table, surrounded by a CROWD seated in haphazard chairs. At the microphone, on a small stage, LAURA is finishing the punchline of a joke.*)

LAURA: ...Know it? I wrote it!

(*The audience breaks into laughter and applause.*)

CHARLOTTE: (*Standing and whistling:*) Woo! Laura! (*To Randy:*) She is so funny! Isn't she funny?

RANDY: Yeah. Funny.

LAURA: (*Bowing:*) Thank you! Thank you! You've been great!

(*Laura returns to the table.*)

RANDY: (*Looking toward the stage:*) Great! <u>Another</u> "guitarist"?

CHARLOTTE: You think you're the only person entitled to be a musician. Other people can play the guitar.

RANDY: Not as well as me.

CHARLOTTE: Anyway—great job, Laura. Your stand-up was phenomenal! I wish I was half as funny as you are.

LAURA: Well I wish I had half your good looks, so that makes us even.

CHARLOTTE: *(Laughing:)* How about I make you a deal—you can have half of Randy and then we'll call it even!

LAURA: Oh, really? Gee, thanks! Which half can I have? The totally egotistical half, or the completely self-centered half? I'll pass, thank you.

RANDY: Nice. What is this? Pick on Randy day?

LAURA: Yes. *(To Charlotte:)* Why don't you do something next week?

CHARLOTTE: Do you remember the talent show in 5th grade? To this day, I can't even look at a marshmallow without crying. I think my role as "Audience Member #7" is the best role for me. You and Randy can have the stage. I'm just not naturally funny.

RANDY: Who cares! You don't have to be funny when you're sweet, and loving and beautiful.

(Randy kisses Charlotte. Laura stands.)

Where are you going?

LAURA: Gotta go.

CHARLOTTE: Before Randy plays?

LAURA: I've heard it before. I'm working on a new painting—oils this time.

RANDY: So what you're saying is, we're less interesting than watching paint dry?

LAURA: Pretty much. Tonight has really inspired me. See you tomorrow. Text me!

CHARLOTTE: I will!

RANDY: Will do!

LAURA: I was talking to Charlotte, Slash.

RANDY: You'll be sorry when I'm famous!

CHARLOTTE: Bye! I'll text you!

(Laura exits. Randy takes out his guitar and tunes it quietly. Charlotte sits looking at him.)

RANDY: What?

CHARLOTTE: So you really don't think I'm funny? At all?

RANDY: You're the one who said you were no good at it, not me.

CHARLOTTE: But couldn't you at least be a little encouraging?

RANDY: I should encourage you to do things you tell me you don't want to do?

CHARLOTTE: Well, no...yes...I don't know! You know what I mean!

RANDY: No, actually, I don't.

CHARLOTTE: You like Laura because she's funny and talented and I'm not!

RANDY: Charlotte, where is this coming from? I'm up next as soon as Joe finished "Stairway to Heaven," which only gives me 23 minutes to tune up. Besides, you're funny...looking.

(Charlotte begins to cry.)

(Sincerely:) Oh, God! I'm sorry, I'm sorry—I was trying to lighten the mood, not make you cry!

CHARLOTTE: Sometimes it feels like you don't love me anymore!

RANDY: Where is this coming from? I do! I swear!

CHARLOTTE: How can someone like you love someone like me?

RANDY: Because you're so cute. Even when you cry and scrunch your face all up like this.

(He makes a face and Charlotte laughs.)

CHARLOTTE: I'm sorry. I can't help it — I know.

RANDY: I love you. I do.

(He kisses her.)

CHARLOTTE: I love you too.

(Randy's phone vibrates. He reads the text.)

RANDY: I have to go.

CHARLOTTE: What?!

RANDY: It's my mom. She said I have to come home.

CHARLOTTE: But you didn't even get to go yet!

RANDY: We'll get here early next week. She hasn't forgotten about that D I got on the last Spanish test. I'm lucky she let me out at all.

CHARLOTTE: I'm sorry you ever taught her how to text.

RANDY: Me too. Gotta go. I'll text when I'm home.

(He runs out.)

CHARLOTTE: Oh. Okay. I love you!

(She comes downstage.)

I think trust is important in a relationship. That's a stupid thing to say. Who doesn't think trust is important? Raise your hand. See? Not one hand. I used to date this guy who never believed anything I said. He'd check my texts and calls. Nothing I said convinced him. Every time I said I loved him he told me he didn't believe me. I worked so hard to change that, threw all of myself into convincing him, that by the time he finally believed me, I didn't love him anymore. It was a lie. And he was finally right.

(She exits.)

SCENE 3 — GEORGE

(George enters on his bike.)

GEORGE: That was our spot. Right there. Parks are good for spots. And that one was ours. Is ours. It'll always be ours — no matter what. It's where we would eat her peanut butter and jelly sandwiches. And black and white cookies. She took the vanilla part. I always took chocolate. It's the spot where I asked her to be my girlfriend. We snuck away from the group and took a walk. We stopped here. And we always came back. We talked about everything here. There is something about this spot that let us really open up to each other. This was good because Laura was never any good at expressing her feelings. I guess. She's the only one who's ever loved me like that. How could anyone else love me as much as she did? It doesn't matter. It was the spot where our relationship began. And it was the spot where it ended. She held me close. Like always. But instead of "I love you." She said "I...can't do this. Anymore." She let go, like it was easy. I just wonder what would have happened if... It doesn't matter. I'll always come back to this spot. But I don't think I can ever have another peanut butter and jelly sandwich.

(He exits.)

SCENE 4 — KISS MONTAGE

(MUSIC plays as LUKE, ROXANNE, Laura, George, Charlotte, Randy, Wendy and Eddie enter and face out.)

LUKE: My first kiss was —

ROXANNE: Disgusting!

LUKE: I was so nervous.

ROXANNE: I thought it was time to move things to a more "mature" level in our relationship. I was eleven.

LUKE: All I remember thinking was "Please, God, don't let me throw up in her mouth!"

LAURA: The first time I kissed a guy he tasted like cigarettes. It was gross...but somehow exciting.

GEORGE: It was on our first date. We went ice skating.

LAURA: The only other word that comes to mind is "wet."

GEORGE: She didn't know how to skate. She was falling all over the place. Once she got it, we had a great time.

CHARLOTTE: My friends dared me to kiss Jimmy Harper. So I did.

GEORGE: Then I leaned over to kiss her.

CHARLOTTE: He was older than me, really hot, but I thought I was cute and irresistible.

GEORGE: She slipped and fell backwards on the ice. Cracked her skull. There was blood.

CHARLOTTE: Evidently, Jimmy didn't think so. He made Timmy Reynolds kiss me instead. Woo hoo.

GEORGE: Then the ambulance came. And her parents. I don't think I've ever been that embarrassed.

LAURA: I used to think it was sexy to show guys how strong you were. So all through grammar school I used to beat them up. And kiss them.

RANDY: My first kiss? It was last night. With your mom!

LAURA: I've kissed a lot of guys.

RANDY: I'm just kidding. No I'm not! It was your mom!

LAURA: But I'm still waiting for my first real kiss. You know, the one where the earth moves and the angels sing and you know you've found the right person. What if that never happens?

RANDY: I'm a really good kisser. *(He looks at Charlotte who continues to stare straight ahead:)* Right?

WENDY: It was in the movies. I picked a scary movie so I'd have an excuse to sit really close. I hardly even saw any of the movie because I was sitting with my face turned up towards him so that when he decided to kiss me, I'd be ready.

RANDY: I said "I'm a really good kisser, right?"

WENDY: When he turned to kiss me, his mouth tasted too sweet, like raspberry candy. And I didn't know what to do with my tongue. So I stuck it in his mouth. He seemed to like that.

EDDIE: My first kiss happened at Boy Scout Camp.

(For the first time, the characters all turn and look at him, reacting to what he's saying, making fun of him.)

Stop. It wasn't like that. It was the camp nurse's daughter. No, it really was! We snuck out after curfew and met in a tree. We talked about nothing for a little while and then we kissed. It was nice. There was no pressure. It just happened. Next summer there was a new nurse at camp and I never saw the girl again.

ROXANNE: My first kiss was magical.

GEORGE: Dangerous.

RANDY: Sexy.

LAURA: Emotionless.

WENDY: Sticky.

CHARLOTTE: Meant for another guy.

EDDIE: Comfortable. Emotionally. The tree wasn't really that comfortable.

LUKE: But my last kiss? My last kiss was—

ROXANNE: Perfect. *Luke sits w R, they kiss*

(He kisses Roxanne, bending her backwards into a dip, slowly. The other characters leave.)

SCENE 5—THE DANCE

going for a walk / apms her

(MUSIC plays. Roxanne and Luke come together in a dance.)

LUKE: Where do you want to go tonight? A movie?

ROXANNE: Let's just hang out at home, okay?

LUKE: What's wrong?

ROXANNE: Nothing. Why does something have to be wrong?

LUKE: It doesn't.

ROXANNE: It's nothing.

LUKE: What's nothing?

ROXANNE: Nothing's nothing.

LUKE: But you just said "it's." "It's" is something.

ROXANNE: "It's" is nothing. It is nothing.

LUKE: Come closer.

ROXANNE: I'm as close as I can get.

LUKE: Then why do you feel so far away?

ROXANNE: We should stop. You have to be up early for tomorrow's audition.

LUKE: The audition is nothing.

ROXANNE: It's always been something.

LUKE: What about you? Don't you have that orientation tomorrow?

ROXANNE: The orientation is nothing.

LUKE: It's always been something.

ROXANNE: Don't miss your audition. It's your last year.

LUKE: What movie do you want to see tonight?

ROXANNE: Don't worry about me.

LUKE: Is that the one with Tom Hanks?

ROXANNE: Go to your audition.

LUKE: I don't think they have that on Netflix.

ROXANNE: We can't watch a movie every day.

LUKE: But can we talk every day. On the phone?

ROXANNE: Yes.

LUKE: Will I see you on the weekends?

ROXANNE: Let's watch *Casablanca*.

LUKE: We always watch *Casablanca*.

ROXANNE: We never watch *Casablanca*.

LUKE: Will I see you on the weekends?

ROXANNE: We don't have to watch *Casablanca*.

LUKE: Okay — whatever you want. Okay?

ROXANNE: Maybe.

LUKE: Let's watch *Casablanca.*

(They dance off.)

SCENE 6 — THE "TALK"

WENDY: When I was ten, my parents decided it was time to have "the talk." Actually, my mom decided and sort of ambushed my dad into it. I came down for breakfast on Sunday morning and my mom announced we were all going to have breakfast together. This was unusual since my mom usually had a slice of toast and a vitamin and my dad had coffee and cigarettes. As far as I knew, I was the only one who ever had "breakfast" in that house. When I sat down, my mom said "We need to talk about the birds and the bees." She's a euphemistic woman. My dad is more direct. He said, "Noreen, if we're going to talk about it, we're going to call it sex." I find that you can never burst into flames when you most need to. My mom was going on, euphemistically, and my dad was correcting her. "Wendy, men have a "boilerplate", and women have a persimmon." He didn't really say "boilerplate" and "persimmon" but you get the idea. My mom gets hung up on details. For some reason, she wanted to make absolutely sure I knew exactly what it took to make a baby. She kept repeating "The "squib" goes into the "mizzenmast." The "squib" goes into the "mizzenmast." The "squib" goes into the "mizzenmast." She said it 18 times. By the 19th time, I snapped. "I GOT the "mizzenmast!" And I ran out of the room, mortified. That was the last time anyone ever talked about "waffle irons" in my house again!

TRANSITION 1

(George rides his bike across the stage. He is wearing a helmet and a reflective vest. The bike has a headlight. He is listening to music. This is his nightly "therapy." He rides onstage, makes a loop, stops, looks off at something in the distance, and rides off.)

SCENE 7—THE PARK

(On the screen appears the following text conversation.)

TEXT A: "My nana's is so boring. this sucks. i miss you."

TEXT B: "I miss u2. u looked so cute b4 <3"

TEXT A: "Im gunna get out of here. want to meet me????"

TEXT B: "in the park???"

TEXT A: "...yes. Half an hour"

TEXT B: "love you—see you their"

(The text screen whites out. We see two silhouettes come together and kiss. They move downstage and sit on a park bench where they continue to kiss. The lights come up to reveal Randy and Laura. Throughout the following, the character remaining on the bench freezes whenever the other breaks away. Randy leaps up and comes downstage.)

RANDY: Look. I know what you're thinking. But I'm not that guy. This isn't who I really am. I know this looks bad. *(He looks at Laura:)* Really bad. I didn't mean for it to happen...This...Us. It just...did. Anything I say to you is going to make me seem superficial and shallow. Sometimes I think I am. A lot of times I think I don't deserve this.

(He sits back down on the bench and they kiss more. Laura comes downstage.)

LAURA: I knew what I was getting into. I went into this with my eyes open. He's dating my best friend. I don't even know how it happened. It just did. How it happened doesn't really matter does it? It's not like if I say, "Oh, on the day I was orphaned in a tragic car accident, Randy stood by me and our love blossomed from there." It's not like A. you'll buy it, or B. it was true. It's not. My parents are both still alive, unfortunately. He was hot. Something clicked. It wasn't on purpose.

(She sits. They kiss. Randy comes downstage.)

RANDY: Okay, okay—I know I don't deserve it. I'm a schmuck. A user. A coward. I keep pretending like I can do this and no one will ever get hurt. Some sick and twisted part of me truly believes that if we could all be honest and open with how we feel that everyone would be much happier. Why can't I love two people? Why do I have to choose? Isn't there enough love in me to go around? There is. I know there is.

(He sits. They kiss. Laura comes downstage.)

LAURA: Pretty much I don't even think about it. It doesn't help, it doesn't change anything. I just try to live in the moment, enjoy the little time we have like this, and pray that it doesn't destroy us all in the end. But it probably will.

(She sits. They kiss. Randy comes downstage.)

RANDY: I feel so guilty. You'd think my guilt would destroy my passion, wouldn't you? Trust me—it doesn't. She's so hot. No, not like that. That makes me sound like a real superficial jerk. I know what you're thinking, "That's right—he's a real superficial jerk." I am. I'm not. There's feelings inside of me that I can't label. Maybe I'm emotionally retarded. Maybe I'm afraid. But I want to be with both of them. And not together. Like I could cut myself in two—one half with Charlotte and one with Laura.

(He sits. They kiss. Laura comes downstage.)

LAURA: It hard, you know? When we're all out together, I just completely detach myself emotionally. Somehow I can manage that. But when I'm alone, and he's not there? I eat myself alive. I imagine terrible things. It makes my stomach hurt. I imagine he makes her laugh more than he makes me laugh. How he kisses her. How it's different from how he kisses me. Better. And I hate them. I hate myself.

(She sits. They kiss. Randy comes downstage.)

RANDY: I know you think I'm a jerk and a horrible human being. But this isn't me. This has become my idea of normal: sneaking around, deleting my texts as soon as they come in. Last week Charlotte went to grab my phone—she was just fooling around. But I knew there were a bunch of texts from Laura. And they were...uh...pretty incriminating. Charlotte kept going after my phone. I didn't want her to see it, didn't want her to find out that way. So I dropped it in the sink. My new $200 phone, floating in a bowl of soapy water because I'm such a coward. But you know the worst part? I was so mad at myself for everything, so pissed at my stupidity, that I let Charlotte believe it was her fault. She was so upset she gave me half the money for it. What am I supposed to do with that? There's $100 sitting in my sock drawer. How can I spend it?

(He sits. They kiss. Blackout.)

TRANSITION 2

(MUSIC plays. Roxanne and Luke enter from opposite sides of the stage, meet in the middle, dance for a moment and tango off.)

SCENE 8—THE GUN

CHARLOTTE: It's hard to date people when your dad's a cop. Guys are always freaked out by it. My dad doesn't help either. One time I was saying good night to a date on the front porch.

He reached over and gave me a kiss—it was a little kiss. But the window was right behind his head. I thought the blinds were closed. But the next thing I hear is this metallic tapping on the glass. My date turns around and all he can see is the barrel of my dad's .45. Tap, tap, tap. He took off running down the street. Strangely, we never had a second date.

(She exits.)

SCENE 9—GUESS WHO?

(Eddie is painting a huge banner that lays across the floor. He tries to hang it up. It falls. He tries again. It hangs limply. It reads: CONGRATULATIONS WENDY! Wendy appears, sitting at the edge of stage left. Her back is to the banner.)

WENDY: I failed.

(Eddie's eyes widen. He hurriedly tries to remove the banner.)

For the fourth time.

(She turns around to find Eddie on the floor, wrapped up in paper.)

What are you doing?

EDDIE: Uh...wallpapering

WENDY: I don't get it—you drive over <u>one</u> cone and it's like you murdered someone! And I definitely stopped at that stop sign! It was a nice, fast stop too!

EDDIE: You'll get it next time.

WENDY: Stop signs are ridiculous. I fail at life.

EDDIE: No, you don't. And you won't even need your license. I can drive you where ever you need to go!

WENDY: You're going to bring me on my dates and stuff?

EDDIE: *(A little hurt:)* Good point.

WENDY: Merr. Sorry, I'm so whiney.

EDDIE: You? Whiney? Nah.

WENDY: (*Laughs:*) Yeah. I'm pathetic.

EDDIE: You're not pathetic. Who cares! So what if you suck at driving?! So what if you knocked over a couple cones?! It doesn't matter because the things you don't suck at trump everything else.

WENDY: (*Smiles:*) Thanks, Eddie.

EDDIE: You know what moments like this call for...?

WENDY: Guess Who?!

EDDIE: Yes!

> (*Eddies runs offstage and grabs his "Guess Who?" board game. He runs back on and sets it up.*)

Okay. But I refuse to use any of the girl cards. There's only four of them!

WENDY: Edward, that's cheating.

EDDIE: I don't care. It's stupid. This game is misogynistic—there should be an equal amount of girl cards, that's all I'm saying.

WENDY: All right. Is your person a girl? (*Laughs:*) Just kidding. Does your person have blonde hair?

EDDIE: No.

> (*Wendy puts down some of her cards.*)

You know, when you think about it this is a really Nazi-ish kind of game. We're eliminating people based on their features.

WENDY: Maybe they should rename it "Eugenics."

(They laugh. Wendy continues to play as Eddie turns to the audience.)

EDDIE: I wonder if she knows... Do you think she knows? Girls are tricky that way. You can never tell what they're thinking. They have this way of being completely mysterious in everything they say. Maybe deep down she knows how she feels about me. One day, it'll just hit her, while she's brushing her teeth or something and she'll realize "I like Eddie!"

(Eddie goes back to the game. Wendy turns to the audience.)

WENDY: I really like this guy Jack. He's super cute. I could definitely see myself with someone like him. Strong, funny, smooth, captain of the swimming team... Maybe I should ask Eddie what he thinks of him... But, I don't know, Eddie's never really liked anyone that I've dated.

(Wendy goes back to the game. Eddie turns to the audience.)

EDDIE: I need to tell her. But she's been talking to this oaf Jack. This is what I'm talking about—mixed messages! What does he have that I don't? So he can swim, big deal! I can...do things too! *(He turns to look at Wendy:)* Oh God, look at her. She's so beautiful, all that flowing hair.

WENDY: *(To Eddie:)* So I've tried this new thing where I don't wash my hair.

EDDIE: Ew. What?

(Wendy hits him playfully.)

WENDY: Shut up. I still use conditioner. It helps my hair. Feel.

(She lifts up her hair for Eddie to feel it. He pats it awkwardly.)

No, run your fingers through it.

EDDIE: Uh. Okay.

(He obliges. It's terribly awkward.)

WENDY: Feels good, huh?

EDDIE: Oh yes. I mean, yeah, it's nice.

(Without thinking he puts her hair to his nose and smells it. Wendy gives him a look like "Um, what are you doing?")

...Sorry.

WENDY: You should try just using conditioner one day. It's great.

EDDIE: Yeah.

(Awkward silence.)

So what are you up to Friday night?

WENDY: Oh. I have to supervise my brother's party at Chuck E. Cheese.

EDDIE: Good times.

WENDY: I gotta run. I'll talk to you later.

(She gets up and exits the stage on her hands. Eddie watches her leave and then looks out.)

EDDIE: God, I love that.

(He exits.)

TRANSITION 3

(Angry-sounding MUSIC plays. George enters stage right on his bike, crosses to stage left and exits.)

SCENE 10 — THE CAKE

(Roxanne and Luke are happily frosting a cake. Eddie enters on the opposite side of the stage and looks out.)

EDDIE: Luke and I are inseparable. *(Looks towards Luke and Roxanne:)* Well, we used to be.

ROXANNE: *(To Luke:)* Whoa! Careful with the sprinkles!

LUKE: Oh, sorry.

EDDIE: Did you hear that? Careful with the sprinkles? She's so controlling!

LUKE: How's it look so far?

ROXANNE: More frosting on this side.

EDDIE: And demanding! Luke never used to worry about where he sprinkled...awkward. I hate myself. And he definitely wouldn't let some girl tell him how to make a cake. Who makes cakes together? You know, if a miracle ever happens and I ever end up in Wendy's pan—with Wendy, then she would <u>want</u> to hang out with my other friends! And by other friends, I mean Luke. She's that kind of wonderful girl. All Roxanne ever wants to do is hang out with Luke and nobody else. She probably doesn't care about me at all.

ROXANNE: So how's Eddie doing?

EDDIE: All right—that's not fair.

LUKE: I don't know. Haven't seen much of him lately. He always seems too preoccupied with Wendy.

EDDIE: Is he serious? Me preoccupied with Wendy? When was the last time he invited me to the movies with him and Roxanne? Yeah, also awkward. I'm the third wheel. I'm going to live the rest of my life as the third wheel. I'll never find my own wheel. I'll never be a bicycle. I'll always be the big, honking wheel on some little girl's tricycle. That's me. Eddie the third wheel.

ROXANNE: He likes Wendy?

EDDIE: He better not—

LUKE: Yeah. Where have you been?

EDDIE: I'm gonna kill 'em.

ROXANNE: That's never going to happen.

EDDIE: Excuse me?

LUKE: Why not? Eddie's a great guy.

EDDIE: This is why we're friends.

ROXANNE: Eddie isn't the kind of guy Wendy's interested in.

LUKE: Why not?

EDDIE: Yeah, why not?

ROXANNE: He's too nice.

LUKE: What?

EDDIE: Typical.

ROXANNE: Plus, he's really awkward.

EDDIE: I don't know where she gets that from.

ROXANNE: And they're friends. It would be like dating her brother.

EDDIE: Why does everyone say that!? I'm not friends with my brother!

LUKE: We were friends before we dated.

ROXANNE: Yeah, but...you're not Eddie.

EDDIE: What is <u>that</u> supposed to mean?

(Luke "accidently" puts frosting on Roxanne's nose.)

LUKE: Oops.

ROXANNE: Oh, it's okay. Don't worry about it.

(Roxanne takes a bigger chunk of frosting and smears it on Luke's mouth. They laugh together.)

LUKE: Hey! This tastes pretty good.

ROXANNE: That's because I made it.

EDDIE: This is disgusting.

LUKE: I love you.

ROXANNE: Do you really?

LUKE: Why don't you ever believe me?

ROXANNE: Prove it.

LUKE: Why do I have to prove it? Isn't it enough proof that I'm here?

ROXANNE: How is that proof? Where else would you be?

LUKE: I don't know... Nowhere.

EDDIE: Nowhere? *Nowhere?* What about with me?

ROXANNE: I knew it.

(They kiss. Eddie moves towards their scene.)

EDDIE: That's it! I'm done.

ROXANNE: *(Looking at the cake:)* I hope he likes it.

(Eddie stops paying attention to Luke and Roxanne.)

EDDIE: I hope they have a great time together.

LUKE: Of course he will.

EDDIE: Don't you ever wish you could put people in their place? Just come right through and give them exactly what they deserve?

(Eddie enters Luke and Roxanne's scene.)

LUKE: Eddie!

ROXANNE: We've made—

(Eddie takes the cake and shoves it in both their faces. He storms off.)

—a cake for your birthday.

(Blackout.)

TRANSITION 4

(MUSIC plays. Laura comes onstage with a can of paint. She goes upstage to the screen and paints. It is an angry, red mass of lines and abstract shapes. She considers it for a moment, waves her hands and erases it. She paints again, rapidly, considers it and erases it again. This is her nightly therapy. She exits.)

SCENE 11 — VIDEO GAMES

RANDY: I'm afraid of the dark, which really sucks because my house is haunted. The ghost constantly bangs on the walls and moves around in the shadows. I know you think I'm crazy but my whole family sees it. It really used to freak me out when I was little. My mom tried to give it a funny name so I'd be less afraid. Now I hate when I'm home alone and Larry knocks on my wall and shut off the lights. It scares the living hell out of me.

(Randy moves downstage and joins George to play chess. Charlotte is reading.)

You know, George, you really suck at this.

GEORGE: I wanted to play N64.

CHARLOTTE: You guys and video games. It kills me.

RANDY: Well, you may have noticed, Charlotte, that we are not playing video games.

(Randy takes George's bishop.)

GEORGE: Aw, not my bishop, Randy!

RANDY: Sorry, George, you're too dependent on your bishop anyway. Learn to move some other pieces around.

GEORGE: But I like the bishop!

CHARLOTTE: There's lots of opportunities for you out there, Georgie. How come you're not seeing anyone?

GEORGE: Well, Lotte, I don't know if you noticed but eight months ago your best friend kicked my guts out emotionally.

CHARLOTTE: It wasn't eight months ago, George.

GEORGE: September 26, [current year], AD, at 9:49 PM Eastern standard time. That makes it seven months, one week, 4 days and...22 hours. I don't bother counting the minutes.

CHARLOTTE: Suddenly, I feel a little uncomfortable. That's not healthy, George.

GEORGE: Neither is getting dumped on your birthday.

RANDY: You're going to lose that pawn.

GEORGE: No, I'm not.

CHARLOTTE: Still, this isn't healthy. You need to move on.

RANDY: Charlotte, guys don't talk about these things.

CHARLOTTE: I wasn't talking to you, Randy. Maybe George wants to talk about it. Did you ever think of that?

RANDY: Why don't you ask him, then?

CHARLOTTE: George, do you want to talk about it?

GEORGE: Not really.

RANDY: Told you so. If you lose that rook you're going to be in check.

CHARLOTTE: I'm sick of you, Randy. All you ever do lately is criticize me!

RANDY: Since when is being right being critical? I just know George better than you.

CHARLOTTE: It's always a competition. I'm going home.

RANDY: Okay — I'll text you later.

CHARLOTTE: You never get it, do you?

(She leaves in a huff.)

RANDY: Wanna play Super Smash Bros.?

GEORGE: Sure.

(They pick up the controllers, sit on the floor and play in silence for a long moment.)

SCENE 12 — DECONSTRUCTION

Luke + Rox watch it like a movie

(Roxanne and Luke enter on the opposite side. George and Randy stay put, still playing.)

LUKE: Ah — see, Roxanne? This is what I was telling you about. Men and women perceive things differently.

ROXANNE: That's true — I think if there's anything we've learned in our relationship, it's that men and women don't function on the same plane of existence.

LUKE: Why don't we see what went right and wrong here.

(The scene resets to the beginning with Roxanne and Luke standing on the opposite side.)

RANDY: You know, George, you really suck at this.

LUKE: Actually, George really does suck at chess. I suck at chess too, but I wouldn't bring my queen out so early if I knew I had a weak middle-game.

ROXANNE: Oh, Luke- you're so cute when you're nerdy.

GEORGE: I wanted to play N64.

CHARLOTTE: You guys and video games. It kills me.

ROXANNE: Okay — here's the first problem. I happen to know that Charlotte likes playing video games, too. She's using this as an excuse right now because she feels ignored by Randy.

RANDY: Well, you may have noticed, Charlotte, that we are not playing video games.

LUKE: This is a true statement. They are playing chess.

(Randy takes George's bishop.)

GEORGE: Aw, not my bishop, Randy!

LUKE: And that was a sloppy move on George's part. He should have sacrificed his knight instead.

ROXANNE: I agree with you. But maybe we should focus a little more broadly on what's going on here.

LUKE: Right. Sorry. He's just so terrible. Anyway, what's happening here is that when two guys are together, they like to be busy. Usually it involves an activity where they can beat the crap out of each other. Probably has roots in our hunter-gatherer culture and the dominance of the male in the societal group.

ROXANNE: Wow — someone's been paying attention in Mr. Douglas's class!

LUKE: Thank you!

(He takes a small bow.)

RANDY: Sorry, George, you're too dependent on your bishop anyway. Learn to move some other pieces around.

GEORGE: But I like the bishop!

CHARLOTTE: There's lots of opportunities for you out there, Georgie. How come you're not seeing anyone?

ROXANNE: Whoa — slow down, Charlotte! That's way too analytical for this situation. See, women like to analyze.

They're thinkers. Men are doers. Probably stems back to when it was their job to figure out what to do for dinner when the men came home empty-handed from a hunt. Plus, what she's showing us here is that she also has a hidden agenda. Tipping your hand too early, Sweetie.

GEORGE: Well, Lotte, I don't know if you noticed but eight months ago your best friend kicked my guts out emotionally.

LUKE: Clearly, she hit a nerve.

CHARLOTTE: It wasn't eight months ago, George.

GEORGE: September 26, [current year], AD, at 9:49 PM Eastern standard time. That makes it seven months, one week, 4 days and...22 hours. I don't bother counting the minutes.

LUKE: I'm so embarrassed for him here. You take over.

ROXANNE: Take over? What's there to say? He's obsessed and not over it yet.

CHARLOTTE: Suddenly, I feel a little uncomfortable. That's not healthy, George.

GEORGE: Neither is getting dumped on your birthday.

RANDY: You're going to lose that pawn.

LUKE: He's gonna lose his masculinity if he stays in this room much longer.

GEORGE: No, I'm not.

CHARLOTTE: Still, this isn't healthy. You need to move on.

ROXANNE: She's right but she's way too pushy here. It's not like rubbing your dog's nose in it when he does his business on your carpet. Nobody wants poop on their face.

RANDY: Charlotte, guys don't talk about these things.

LUKE: Too true.

CHARLOTTE: I wasn't talking to you, Randy. Maybe George wants to talk about it. Did you ever think of that?

ROXANNE: I feel sort of bad here because I know she wants to help, but even if George does want to talk about it, he's not going to do it with Randy there.

RANDY: Why don't you ask him, then?

CHARLOTTE: George, do you want to talk about it?

GEORGE: Not really.

ROXANNE: This is a lie.

LUKE: This is the truth.

RANDY: Told you so. If you lose that rook you're going to be in check.

LUKE: This is really interesting. See what Randy did there? He's giving George respect and space by acting normally. See how he just ignores the entire subject? Brilliant! Kudos, Randy!

CHARLOTTE: I'm sick of you, Randy. All you ever do lately is criticize me!

ROXANNE: He does seem to criticize her a lot in front of other people.

RANDY: Since when is being right being critical? I just know George better than you.

CHARLOTTE: It's always a competition. I'm going home.

ROXANNE: Good—I wanted to show this to you. This is a classic play. But a risky one for Charlotte. It's win or lose. Charlotte does not really want to go home. She wants Randy to stop her. In her mind, it's a demonstration of his feelings for her. If he loves her, he won't let her go. If he lets her go, it means she's less important than A. George, B. chess, and C. Probably socks.

LUKE: This is true. In three words, Charlotte has given Randy the ultimate test in their relationship. But does Randy hear this? No. Women's logic is at a frequency totally incompatible with men's brain function. What Randy hears is this: "It's time for me to go. Thanks for a great evening. I'm going home."

RANDY: Okay—I'll text you later.

CHARLOTTE: You never get it, do you?

LUKE: Epic fail on Randy's part.

ROXANNE: *(Shaking her head sadly:)* Epic fail.

(Charlotte leaves in a huff.)

What you're not able to see is that on the other side of the door, Charlotte has waited a few moments before going up the stairs. She's still pretty sure Randy will stop her from leaving.

LUKE: He won't.

ROXANNE: I know that.

RANDY: Wanna play Super Smash Bros.?

GEORGE: Sure.

(They pick up the controllers, sit on the floor and play in silence for a long moment.)

LUKE: This is perhaps the pinnacle of male interaction. It looks like they're completely absorbed in their own worlds, but really what's going on here is a deep bonding—an emotional exchange that women will never, ever understand. See, if Randy didn't care about George, he would have run away as soon as someone mentioned Laura. But the exchange that is happening now says "I love you, man. I love you and care about you enough to sit here, seventeen inches away—no closer! —and share this game with you. And when we team up together to kick the crap out of Bowser and bring him to his knees, sobbing like a little girl who dropped her ice cream cone, I am pretending it's Laura. Every punch I throw is for every second she broke your poor heart."

ROXANNE: Oh, Luke—that's beautiful!

LUKE: *(A strange mix of pride and embarrassment:)* Thanks!

ROXANNE: And really sexy!

(She jumps up in his arms and kisses him. Luke carries her off. Blackout.)

SCENE 13—FACEBOOK STALKING 1

(George is on Laura's Facebook page. We see the pages on the screen behind him.)

GEORGE: The first thing Laura did when we broke up was to remove all traces of me from her Facebook. All wall posts, photos, gifts, comments. Everything. She should work for the FBI because she eradicated me so completely that for a moment I wasn't sure if I ever really existed. Wow. That sounded pathetic and codependent, like I needed to be part of her life to be happy. It's not true. It's just that I was happier then. Look at this. Relationship Status: Single. Interested in: Men; Looking for: Relationship, Whatever. Whatever is right. *(Composes himself a little:)* I sound like a nut-job. I have all these emotions and lately, they've been sneaking out the back-door and coming around to the front and really scaring the crap out of me. That just sounded wrong. I can't even think straight. *(Closes the laptop:)* It was my fault really. She said I wasn't "sensitive enough." It's really ironic because now all I am is a big blubbering pile of sensitivity and raw nerves. It's really sort of funny in a way. I never used to get angry or cry or feel sad about things. For 17 years I never really had those emotions. Now they're the only things I feel. It worries me a little.

(He exits.)

TRANSITION 5

(MUSIC plays. Eddie enters and sits Up-Center. Wendy enters on her hands and walks around him once and then gently back-walk-over's offstage. Eddie is enraptured. He goes to follow her, thinks better of it and exits in the opposite direction.)

SCENE 14 — THE NOTE & THE MOON

(Roxanne enters.)

ROXANNE: I was in love with Billy Logan. We were in 7th grade and he was the cutest, most shy and timid boy I'd ever met. I just wanted to put him in my pocket. It was Sadie Hawkins day and I believed almost everything my teacher told us. I cornered Billy by his locker and told him I wanted him to come out with me sometime. He was nervous and surprised. He said "No." I went home and cried. He wrote me a note the next day. It said "Yes, I'd like to go out with you sometime." I cried again. I still have the note.

(She exits. Luke enters.)

LUKE: I liked this girl since the minute I saw her. She was perfect. There was just one thing standing in our way — she happened to be a celebrity. I hate those minor technicalities. Just because you like someone who is "famous" people automatically start putting these labels on you — you're "one of those." So what, she's beautiful, we have exactly the same things in common — she just happens to be on People's Hottest 25 Under 25 List. So I did what any normal guy would do when he wants to pursue a girl: stand in line at her CD signing. I thought, all right, this is it. The minute she sees me, I won't have to say anything. We won't need words. She'll take me in her arms and I'll spirit her away to her limo and...well, you know the rest. So I was standing on line, acting real cool, with a dozen roses in my hand and a piece of the moon. That's right, a piece of the moon that I bought for $29.99 from the lunar registry. It was actually just a certificate that said I purchased a plot on the moon, not an actual piece of the moon. What? I needed a back up just in case she didn't fall in love with me at first sight. So I finally get up to her...I give her the roses. She adds them to the pile. I give her the moon. She looks confused. She signs my CD. I go home. Never buy someone the moon. They won't appreciate it.

(He exits. Blackout.)

SCENE 15 — DINNER CONVERSATION

(Randy and Charlotte are out to dinner.)

CHARLOTTE: What are you getting?

RANDY: I don't know. I like to pick something that I like and then keep that on the side for a back up. Then I go through the rest of the menu to see if I can find something better. But this way, if the waitress comes over, I'm not scrambling to find something — because I have a back up. I never like to be left without a backup.

CHARLOTTE: You're weird.

RANDY: Shut up.

(Randy's phone BUZZES. He looks at it and answers his text.)

CHARLOTTE: Are you seriously texting during our dinner?

RANDY: It's my mom.

(Lights up on the other side of the stage. Laura sits on her couch, phone in hand.)

CHARLOTTE: Your mom makes you smile like that?

RANDY: What? My mom's funny.

CHARLOTTE: I've met your mom.

RANDY: What's with you always harping on my mom, huh?

CHARLOTTE: She hates me.

RANDY: She does not.

CHARLOTTE: Randy. Whenever I come over, all she does is look at me like this-

(She makes a nasty, disapproving face.)

RANDY: Real nice, Charlotte.

CHARLOTTE: She always acts like I'm taking you away from her. Like I'm corrupting your innocence or something.

RANDY: She does not.

CHARLOTTE: Your innocence was corrupted long before you met me.

RANDY: Yeah. Definitely.

CHARLOTTE: Why is it that I always feel like I'm the only one in this relationship?

RANDY: Too true. Too true.

CHARLOTTE: Would you stop with the texting!?

RANDY: Okay, Charlotte, I'll just tell my mother to shut the hell up.

CHARLOTTE: You're putting words in my mouth.

RANDY: Maybe she's fallen down the stairs because her appendix exploded and she needs my help.

CHARLOTTE: She does!?

RANDY: No. I meant what if. And why would she text me if she fell down a flight of stairs?

CHARLOTTE: I don't know, I don't know! I don't know why she's texting you at all.

RANDY: All right, all right. I'm putting the phone down. Happy?

CHARLOTTE: *(Taking his hand:)* Randy, what's gotten into you? I feel like you're not even here. I feel like you're somewhere else. And I'm just having dinner with your shadow.

(Randy gets up from the table and joins Laura on the couch. Charlotte stays engaged in her scene as if Randy is still there.)

Where have you been?

LAURA: Where have you been?

RANDY: Sorry. I got lost.

LAURA: It's always the same excuse.

RANDY: I'm here now.

(He sits down and kisses her. She pulls away.)

LAURA: I don't want your pity kiss. You said you'd be here.

RANDY: I'm sorry. I'm really sorry. I don't know what's gotten into me.

CHARLOTTE: It's okay.

CHARLOTTE: I've missed you.   **LAURA:** I've missed you.

RANDY: I've missed you too.

LAURA: I don't feel like I'm that important to you. I'm tired of being your backup.

CHARLOTTE: I just need to know that you'll be here.

RANDY: I'm here for you.

CHARLOTTE: Okay. I believe you.

LAURA: I want to believe you.

RANDY: What do I have to do to prove myself to you?

CHARLOTTE: Just love me.

LAURA: Love me.

RANDY: I do love you.

LAURA: We've got to tell her.

RANDY: We can't.

CHARLOTTE: Tell me what's bothering you.

RANDY: I don't want to.

LAURA: So we're just going to be stuck in this forever?

CHARLOTTE: What are you afraid of?

RANDY: It'll ruin everything.

LAURA: You're right.

CHARLOTTE: You're wrong.

RANDY: I want this to work out for all...both of us.

CHARLOTTE: It will. We're worth it.

LAURA: Sometimes I wonder if it's even worth it.

RANDY: It's worth it.

LAURA: Show me.

RANDY: I'll show you.

CHARLOTTE: You don't have to show me. I believe you.

(*Randy kisses Laura passionately.*)

RANDY: Do you believe me?

(*Randy gets up and joins Charlotte back at the table.*)

CHARLOTTE: I believe you.   **LAURA:** I believe you.

(Randy sits and stares at his menu.)

CHARLOTTE: Randy? Randy? Hello!? What are you having?

(Randy is shaken out of his reverie. He looks out.)

RANDY: This is why I always have a backup.

(Blackout.)

SCENE 16—MY BELT

GEORGE: Two summers ago I was hanging around town with my friends and we ran into another group of friends. They'd been drinking. Laura was with them and she was pretty drunk and falling all over me. I liked her and I guess she knew it. She was really aggressive, saying "I know you want me" and stuff like that, which wasn't like her at all. She came up really close and I thought she was going to kiss me and suddenly she starts undoing my belt. I was fifteen. Be honest—what would you have done? Well, she got the belt undone, pulled it out of the loops and ran away with it. I tried to chase after her, but my pants kept falling down so I had to run and hold them up. She got in the car and they drove off with my good belt! It took me two weeks to get the nerve up to call and ask for it back. I really need that belt to keep my pants up.

TRANSITION 6

(MUSIC plays. Randy enters followed by Charlotte. They are clearly in the middle of a fight. They gesticulate and shout silently. Charlotte storms off. Randy follows her.)

Somone s
headphones?

SCENE 17 — DAYDREAM MONTAGE

(Randy, Luke, Roxanne, Charlotte, Eddie, Laura, George, and Wendy are sitting in class. The teacher drones on, pointlessly, monotonously, until the sound dissolves completely.)

TEACHER (V.O.): In order to understand Spanish, one must understand the cultures of Spanish-speaking countries. Mexico, for example, was founded during...uh...the later half of the Age of Exploration by Fernando Cortez. Prior to this, Mexico had been ruled...uh...by the Aztec Empire for centuries. The Aztecs inhabited a city called Tenochitlan, which is now modern-day Mexico City...

(The CLOCK TICKS loudly.)

LUKE: I hate this class. Who needs Business Spanish? "¿Le gustaría comprar una bicicleta? ¿Cuánto es el lápiz de color rojo? Voy a tomar más de su empresa y dejar sin hogar, que viven en la calle como un perro." I wish I could manipulate the fabric of time and space. But I failed Physics and had to go to summer school last year. Maybe I'll just figure out how to build a time machine. Then I can skip right to graduation.

(Laura doesn't speak. Projected on the screen is what she is working on her laptop: a time-lapse drawing of an eye.)

GEORGE: Pretty much I think about what would happen if terrorists tried to take over the school.

(Three terrorists, dressed like NINJAS, burst into the classroom with machine guns. MACHINE GUN FIRE. George jumps out of his seat. All of the students except Laura hit the floor. SCREAMS and COMMOTION. George runs to the Ninjas. He karate chops Ninja 1, who crumples to the floor. He roundkicks Ninja 2, who falls backwards. He makes a threatening move toward Ninja 3 who freezes, begins to cry and runs out the door. George wipes off his hands and sits back down. Everyone congratulates him. Laura runs over and kisses him.)

CHARLOTTE: What would it be like if me and Randy got married?

(Screen switches to a video of Charlotte and Randy at their wedding, in slow motion.)

No, not that dress.

(Screen switches to the same scene. Charlotte is wearing a different dress.)

Ugh — that's hideous. And it makes me look really fat.

(Screen switches to the same scene. Charlotte is wearing a third dress.)

That one's better. We could even change the guy.

(Screen switches to still photos of Charlotte and: George in a tux; Eddie in a tux; Luke in a tux.)

I don't particularly want to be married. I just like to picture the dress. And the shoes.

(Charlotte sits. Laura's drawing comes back on the screen.)

RANDY: George and I usually have the same daydreams.

(Ninjas burst in again. This time they take hostages: Charlotte, Laura and George, holding the guns to their head. SHOUTING in another language. MACHINE GUN FIRE. Roxanne, Eddie and Luke jump up and hide behind Randy. Randy stands and puts his hand out. Using the "Force" he "pulls" a machine gun from Ninja 1. Using short bursts from the gun, he picks off Ninja 1 and Ninja 3.)

EDDIE: *(Momentarily breaking character:)* Why didn't you just disarm all of them with the Force?

RANDY: This is why you don't have a girlfriend. You're so uncool. Get back where you belong. This is my daydream.

(Ninja 2 is using George as a human shield. George is crying.)

GEORGE: Oh, Randy, please help me! I'm too young to die!

RANDY: Religion is the cause of all of the problems in the world. Religious extremism is destroying our planet. Iraq, Darfur, the melting of the Polar ice caps. The migration of the Canadian Goose into New Jersey! I'm sick and tired of walking through goose poop to get to my car!

GEORGE: Uh, Randy?

RANDY: Oh, right.

(Another quick burst from Randy's gun and Ninja 3 drops to the ground. Everyone crowds around Randy. Luke and Eddie pick him up on their shoulders. The girls all clamor to touch him and George kisses his "ring." Randy blesses the crowd like the Pope and waves like the Queen. Patriotic MUSIC plays. Randy sits. A college website appears on the screen.)

ROXANNE: This is the only time I ever have to myself. I go on the Fordham website and look at all the pictures. I picture myself there, meeting new people, going to parties, picking classes. Most people don't believe this, but it's the classes I'm most excited about. There's a whole world out there and I'm going to be a part of it. On my own for the first time in my life. I'm going to live in the city. It's so exciting. I feel awful being excited about leaving Luke. Sometimes I lie awake in bed at night—a mixture of excitement and resentment. I can't talk about it in front of him. He doesn't say anything, but he gets this funny look on his face. I hate it. I love him. How messed up is that?

EDDIE: Look at her. She's perfect. *(He stands, lost in the moment:)* The sun streams in through the chalk-clouded glass/a ray of light falls, soft, on her face/If I had a thousand summers/I would trade them all for one single night/A look, a touch/ Her hand in mine/ Her soft lips, warm and inviting, on my cheek,/On my lips, on my neck, on my — *(He remembers* *where he is:)* Umm...never mind. Awkward. I hate myself. I wrote that for her. I was going to leave it in her locker. But...

(Wendy looks lost in deep thought.)

I wonder if she's thinking about me. Wouldn't that be cool? Me thinking about her, her thinking about me. Someday we can laugh about how we sat two feet apart every day for a year, daydreaming about each other. *(Eddie sits:)* God, please let her be thinking about me.

(Wendy shifts in her seat and looks up.)

WENDY: I wonder what I'll have for lunch today.

(Blackout. End of Act I.)

ACT II

SCENE 1 — SOCCER

(Eddie is sitting on the park bench, writing.)

EDDIE: I'm trying really hard not to be overbearing. I'm like a shark, I go around the edges, you know? I can't just blurt out "I love you, Wendy McGann! You're the most amazing, beautiful, funny, talented girl in the world. I want to spend the rest of my life with you and want you to have my babies." That's coming on too strong. It's true that I want her to walk on her hands right over to me. It's true that she's the last thing I think about before I fall asleep at night and the first thing I think about in the morning. It's true that she's the first person I text on every major holiday including Easter, Arbor Day and Flag Day to show her that I'm thinking about her. That's why we're friends. Because I care. I talk to her. I mean really talk to her. And I listen. Talking and listening are the biggest and most important parts of any relationship, if you ask me. Then again, I wouldn't know. I've never been in a real relationship. Maybe I'm just too hung up on Wendy. Is that possible? *(He considers this seriously:)* No. That thought only lasts a second until I think about the way her hair smells...God, that's creepy.

(Luke enters dribbling a soccer ball.)

LUKE: Hey — wanna play?

(Eddie takes the paper and stuffs it in his pocket.)

EDDIE: No. I suck. The last time we played, every time the ball rolled down the hill you made me go get it.

(Luke does tricks with the ball, showing off a little.)

LUKE: Come on — you're good. I'll get it this time.

EDDIE: Fine. But I'm not going into the river again. I got tetanus from it last year. I had to get a shot.

LUKE: Sheesh — what a baby. Have it your way.

(They begin passing the ball back and forth.)

EDDIE: Did you see Jessica yesterday?

LUKE: What? In those jean shorts?

EDDIE: Actually, I was talking about that shirt.

LUKE: Yeah — that was hot.

EDDIE: Uh, in a slutty way. Not that there's anything wrong with that.

LUKE: You can say that again.

(They pass the ball in silence for a moment, contemplating Jessica.)

So what were you writing?

EDDIE: When?

LUKE: When I got here.

EDDIE: I wasn't writing anything.

LUKE: Yes you were. I saw you. You put it in your back pocket.

(Eddie checks his pocket reflexively.)

EDDIE: No I didn't.

LUKE: Yes you did — it's sticking out.

EDDIE: I don't know what you're talking about.

(Luke purposely kicks the ball behind Eddie. When Eddie turns, he puts him in a headlock.)

Aww! You kicked it down the hill! Hey! What the hell —

LUKE: Say "Uncle"!

EDDIE: Uncle!! Uncle!! Ow!

LUKE: Let me see the paper. Do it or you know what.

EDDIE: No—<u>don't</u>!

LUKE: Three. Two. One.

(Luke begins to tickle Eddie. Eddie screams and convulses.)

EDDIE: Here! Take it! Take it!

(Luke takes the paper and reads.)

LUKE: What is this?

EDDIE: *(Embarrassed:)* Ideas for asking Wendy out...

LUKE: *(Reading from the list:)* Buy her a stylish hand mirror with a card that says "In this mirror you will see the image of the most beautiful woman in the world." Uh...

EDDIE: What? That's romantic, isn't it?

LUKE: Uh...no. *(Reads the list:)* Wait. Memorize one of Shakespeare's sonnets?

EDDIE: Oh, come on. That's a great idea. I'll bring her to a romantic setting...like a botanical garden. And recite it for her.

LUKE: Yeah. Not a great idea.

EDDIE: No, listen! I won't just suddenly start reciting poetry to her. I'll ease into it. I'm like a shark.

LUKE: I wonder where this is going...

EDDIE: We'll just be sitting in there, enjoying the horticulture. I'll turn to her and jokingly say "So is now a good time to recite a love poem to you?"

LUKE: Oh boy.

EDDIE: She'll say "yes" thinking I'm going to recite something funny and stupid like that guy from Nantucket. But instead, I'll catch her off guard. I'll look into her eyes, smile... *(He looks into Luke's eyes and smiles:)* I'll recite the sonnet as I gently stroke her face... *(He gently strokes Luke's face:)* "Shall I compare thee to a summer's day? / Thou art more lovely and more temperate: / Rough winds do shake the darling buds of May..." *(He catches himself:)* ...Awkward. I hate myself.

LUKE: Now can you see why that's a bad idea?

EDDIE: Yeah. I'm an idiot. But there are other good ones on there!

LUKE: *(Reads the list:)* Write her a love song and sing it for her?

EDDIE: That's my favorite.

LUKE: Why don't you write her a rap song?

(Luke and Eddie perform a make-shift rap song. It's pathetic.)

EDDIE: Kick it!

(Luke starts a beat box.)

I'm into Wendy, yo!
I'm into Wendy, yo!
She walks on her hands right over to me,
Doesn't wash her hair, but that's not creepy,
We play board games by Milton Bradley,
When I think about her, I pray she thinks about me.

LUKE: Word.

(When they finish, they stop and look at each other.)

EDDIE: Nah.

LUKE: Nah.

(They exit.)

SCENE 2—CALL WAITING

(Randy walks Center Stage. He's on his cell.)

RANDY: ...so this moron goes "Pepperoni? Is it spicy?" So now I start talking to him like he's a retarded toddler and I go "Well, Sir, it's called PEPPERoni, and the PEPPER part means it's SPICY, like peppers!" And he's like "OOOOhhh!" And I'm like "I'm outta here" and I made Carl make this idiot's sandwich...I know, but he was dumb. People like that shouldn't be allowed to breathe my oxygen...I know...I love you too. You're so adorable.

(Laura enters and stands stage right.)

LAURA: Thanks—you're not too bad yourself.

RANDY: So can you meet me?

LAURA: The park?

RANDY: Yeah. Come on. You're so-

LAURA: I'm so what?

RANDY: Sorry—call waiting. Hang on a sec. Hello?

(Charlotte enters and stands stage left.)

CHARLOTTE: Hey!

RANDY: Oh, hey!

CHARLOTTE: So I got off from work early.

RANDY: Oh...how come?

CHARLOTTE: The frozen yogurt machine blew up. There were fire engines. So can we still make that movie?

RANDY: Oh, uh, I'm not sure. Let me call you back.

CHARLOTTE: Okay.

(Charlotte turns to exit. Randy pushes a button on the phone.)

RANDY: Sorry—that was Charlotte. Mmm. You're so hot. I can't wait to see you.

(Charlotte stops in her tracks and turns around.)

CHARLOTTE: Randy. It's STILL Charlotte. Who was that, your "mom" again?!

RANDY: Ha, ha. I knew it was you. It was just a —

CHARLOTTE: Go to hell!

(Charlotte hangs up and runs off.)

RANDY: —joke. *(He pushes the button again:)* Hey. I'm sorry. It was my mom.

LAURA: Are you okay? You sound sorta funny.

RANDY: Oh, yeah. My grandpa fell but he's going to be all right. My mom's shaken up.

LAURA: Okay. I'll make you feel better soon. See you at our "spot" at 9:30?

RANDY: Yeah. See you then.

(Blackout.)

TRANSITION 1

(MUSIC plays. George rides his bike across the stage and exits.)

SCENE 3—CRISS-CROSS

(Wendy enters on her hands from stage left. Roxanne enters from stage right. They cross each other at center stage.)

WENDY: Oh, excuse me.

ROXANNE: Sorry.

(Wendy sits at the edge of the stage at stage right. Roxanne sits at the edge of the stage at stage left. They both look out.)

WENDY: We went on a date.

ROXANNE: We go on lots of dates.

WENDY: He seemed nice enough.

ROXANNE: He's the nicest guy in the world.

WENDY: He told me he liked me.

ROXANNE: He loves me.

WENDY: I like when he smiles.

ROXANNE: I can't get over his smile.

WENDY: There's something about him.

ROXANNE: There's definitely something about him.

WENDY: I finally let myself get close to someone.

ROXANNE: We're so close.

WENDY: Things got strange.

ROXANNE: But things are getting strange.

WENDY: It's hard to explain.

ROXANNE: I can't find the words for it.

WENDY: He took me to a party.

ROXANNE: We like to stay home and watch movies.

WENDY: We were having fun.

ROXANNE: We have so much fun.

WENDY: But then I mentioned Eddie.

ROXANNE: I slipped about Fordham.

WENDY: He got jealous.

ROXANNE: He's not jealous. He's happy for me.

WENDY: I told him that we're just friends.

ROXANNE: I told him that we'll be okay.

WENDY: I was telling the truth.

ROXANNE: I might be lying.

WENDY: He didn't believe me.

ROXANNE: He believed me.

WENDY: Like an idiot.

ROXANNE: Like an idiot.

WENDY: I have to stop talking about him.

ROXANNE: I can't talk about it with him.

WENDY: I really like Eddie.

ROXANNE: I love Luke.

WENDY: We're best friends.

ROXANNE: He's the best thing that's ever happened to me.

WENDY: But I can't help it.

ROXANNE: I can't help but thinking...

WENDY: Maybe he's...

ROXANNE: Maybe he's just...

WENDY: Holding me back.

ROXANNE: Holding me back.

(Eddie enters from stage left. Luke enters from stage right. They cross each other at center stage.)

EDDIE: Hey.

LUKE: Hey.

(Eddie joins Wendy at stage right. Luke joins Roxanne at stage left.)

Hey, so I was thinking...

EDDIE: I was thinking about you in the shower today...

(Wendy looks confused. Luke and Roxanne stop their scene and look over at Eddie.)

WENDY, LUKE & ROXANNE: What?

EDDIE: ...Awkward. I hate myself.

(Luke goes back to his scene with Roxanne.)

LUKE: Maybe we can watch *Casablanca* tonight?

EDDIE: I tried just using conditioner.

ROXANNE: That'll be good.

WENDY: That's good.

LUKE: Maybe we can go on a vacation together?

EDDIE: Have you ever been to a botanical garden?

ROXANNE: When?

WENDY: When do you want to go?

LUKE: I can get out of work for a week in August.

EDDIE: How 'bout this Saturday?

ROXANNE: I don't know if I can.

WENDY: This Saturday won't work.

LUKE: Oh.

EDDIE: Oh.

ROXANNE: I'll be super busy getting ready...you know.

WENDY: Jack wants to go on another date.

ROXANNE: I'm sorry.

WENDY: I'm sorry.

LUKE: Of course.

EDDIE: Don't worry about it.

ROXANNE: Listen, I gotta run? I'll see you tonight?

WENDY: I gotta go. I'll see you later.

(Luke and Roxanne kiss. Eddie and Wendy hug awkwardly. Wendy and Roxanne exit. Luke and Eddie watch them go. Once they're gone, they look at each other and then down.)

EDDIE: Damn.

LUKE: Damn.

(Blackout.)

SCENE 4 — BREAKUP 1

(Randy and Laura are kissing on the park bench.)

RANDY: Laura...

LAURA: Uh, oh. I know that tone.

RANDY: Laura...

LAURA: I don't want to hear this, Randy. Not right now. Not today.

RANDY: Laura, please.

LAURA: Nope. Not listening to you. Lalala.

RANDY: Okay, okay. Have it your way.

LAURA: I know this day is coming. Just give me tonight. Just one more night.

(He kisses her — a kiss full of longing and desperation and passion. George rides his bicycle upstage. He is wearing a helmet and a reflective vest. He rides off stage left. The sound of the BIKE CRASHING into garbage cans. After a moment, he comes back on foot, slightly disheveled.)

GEORGE: Oh, God.

(Randy and Laura pull apart.)

LAURA: Uh oh.

(Randy jumps up.)

RANDY: Uh...I'm not here. I gotta go.

(He runs offstage. Laura's defense mechanism is sarcastic, self-effacing humor.)

LAURA: Hi, George. What brings you to the park so late at night?

GEORGE: Oh, God. This isn't...this isn't...

LAURA: Yeah. It certainly isn't.

GEORGE: I don't...I don't...Oh, God. Randy?!

LAURA: Yeah. I'm surprised at myself. Pardon my manners — would you like to have a seat?

GEORGE: Our spot. This is our spot.

LAURA: Well, George, last I checked, this was still a public park. You know, those little plaques they put on the benches are honorary rather than territorial.

GEORGE: *(This idea bursts out of him:)* Did you take his belt?!

LAURA: What?

GEORGE: Did. You. Take. His. Belt?

LAURA: What? No? What are you talking about.

GEORGE: *(On the verge of tears:)* His belt, his belt! Did you take it? Like you took mine?

LAURA: No! I was drunk. It was stupid. It didn't mean anything!

GEORGE: *(Small:)* What?

LAURA: Oh, come on! I didn't mean it like that. What's wrong with you? I don't get this!

GEORGE: Don't get this? Don't get this?! You spend every day for two years telling me I'm not sensitive! I'm not in touch with my emotions! I don't cry enough or get angry enough! Well now I'm angry!

LAURA: Okay, this isn't cool. We're in public. We broke up. I can be where I want with anyone I want.

GEORGE: You broke my heart!

LAURA: *(Jumping up:)* You broke my heart, too! But I'm not standing in the park like a freak screaming about it!

GEORGE: I love you.

LAURA: I don't love you. Not anymore.

(George collapses on the bench, sobbing.)

George. Please don't. Not here. Not here. I'm sorry. It wasn't your fault. It wasn't my fault. It's just how it went. We grew apart. I didn't do it on purpose.

(She sits, lost in self-thought.)

Funny. I seem to be involved in a lot of things beyond my control lately. Nothing and everything is my fault. I'm sorry, George. I really am. I have to go.

(She exits.)

GEORGE: But...this was our spot!

(Blackout.)

TRANSITION 2

(MUSIC plays. Luke and Roxanne enter from opposite sides and begin to dance different dances — their movements are disjointed, matching in neither style nor rhythm.)

SCENE 5—FACEBOOK STALKING 2

(Eddie is at his laptop. We see the images from his laptop projected on the screen behind him.)

EDDIE: This is Wendy's Facebook. And it's not creepy that I look at it. I'm just interested in what she's doing. Okay, it is creepy. But I love looking at it. Makes me feel close to her when she's not there. See this pig? I gave her that pig on her birthday last year—when she was little, her mom called her Miss Piggy. *(He snorts like a pig:)* She's got 634 friends. Sometimes I friend her friends, even if I don't know them... Look at all these groups she belongs to. I never even knew there were this many different Sound of Music groups: The Sound of Music Fans three exclamation points; Dame Julie Andrews Rocks; Maria Von Trapp for Sainthood; Maria Von Trapp Is My Ideal Woman; Confidence and Edelweiss... I love her status updates. She's got great taste in music. Look: "Wendy McGann is gonna drive and never ever slow down". "Wendy McGann will write you visions of my summer—quoting lines from all those movies that we love." "Wendy McGann you're what keeps me believing this world's not gone dead, strength in my bones and the words in my head." Isn't that beautiful? Well...she didn't write it, but still, she wrote it in her status. Sometimes I think they're about me and maybe she's trying to tell me something through her status updates. Like they're secretly meant for me... Well, let's look at some pictures. Look at her profile picture—not one single picture taken in the bathroom mirror! Isn't that great? I like this one where she's upside down and all her silky shiny hair is hanging down. God, she's beautiful. Oh, look—Jessica tagged her in a photo. Eww— *(Reading the title of the photo album:)* "There's A Party In My PANTS and Everyone's Invited!" God, Jessica's gross. Her friends are gross. I'm not against drinking, but these people spend 5 out of 7 days planning for it. Get a life, Jessica. *(He clicks on the photo:)* Huh. I didn't think Wendy was hanging out with these people. This was last weekend. I thought she had to go to Chuck E. Cheese.

(He begins flipping through the pictures. Many people have red Solo cups. Wendy does too. Pictures of Wendy: dancing wearing a funny hat; being held aloft by 5 guys; balancing a cup on her head; toasting the camera with Jessica.)

Oh. Umm. Yeah. This is...really sort of...you have to think...I..

(There is a picture of a spin the bottle game in the living room. The next picture shows Wendy kissing Jack. The next picture shows Jack and Wendy kissing outside, clearly caught. Eddie closes his laptop violently.)

I hate Facebook.

(He exits.)

TRANSITION 3

(MUSIC plays. Charlotte is waiting, upstage. George crosses to her. He silently tells her about Randy and Laura. She reacts accordingly and runs off. George, unsure of what to do, hesitates, finally running off after her.)

SCENE 6—THE POWERPOINT

(The room is dark. There is a faint dark blue glow from the screen upstage. Randy enters. We see him in silhouette.)

RANDY: Uh, hello? Charlotte.

(Charlotte shines a flashlight right in Randy's face.)

CHARLOTTE: Hey—sorry. All the power's out.

RANDY: Jesus—get that thing out of my eyes. What the hell is this?!

(He trips over a chair.)

CHARLOTTE: I'm really sorry. Why don't you just sit there until your eyes adjust.

RANDY: Charlotte—

CHARLOTTE: Look. Let's try to handle this like mature adults, okay? I'm hurt and you're upset, but let's try to talk through this and see if there isn't something worth saving, all right?

RANDY: Oh...okay. Ha. I thought you brought me here to kill me or something. Not like you don't have the right to or anything, but—

LAURA: Ow!

(Laura stumbles in the dark, also tripping over a chair.)

RANDY: What's going on?

(Charlotte shines her light on Laura's face.)

LAURA: Randy? Where's Roxanne? She texted me and told me to meet her here. She said she had to tell me something urgent about George.

RANDY: Laura—

CHARLOTTE: Oh, Laura. Thanks for coming. Roxanne couldn't get the car but she told me to give you the message. Why don't you sit down—all the power's out.

(Laura gropes her way to the chair next to Randy and sits.)

LAURA: *(Whispering to Randy:)* What's going on?

CHARLOTTE: Tsk, tsk. Come on Laura—no one likes secrets. Certainly not secrets involving my best friend dating my boyfriend.

(She laughs. The lights snap on, blinding them momentarily. Charlotte has donned a pair of sunglasses moments before the lights snap on.)

That's better. Now where were we?

RANDY: Okay, this is way too weird. I'm outta here!

LAURA: Isn't that disappearing trick getting a little old, Randy?

CHARLOTTE: Oh — hahaha — I'm sorry. Were you planning to leave? You can't leave.

(She motions slightly with her hand. Two NINJAS with ropes jump up from behind Randy's and Laura's chairs, binding them to the seats. They gag them.)

Thank you, Akira, Matsumo.

(The Ninjas salute her and exit.)

I'm sorry — I worked really hard on this PowerPoint and I can't have you leave and miss it. There's 634 slides. *(Proudly:)* I animated them myself!

(One Ninja returns with a drink on a tray. He is dressed like a waiter.)

Thank you, Katsuro. *(Indicating the drink:)* It's a Shirley Temple. Five cherries. Yum. Anyway, where was I? Oh! My PowerPoint!

(Charlotte claps and the lights fade to black except for a spot on each character. The slide show begins. It contains every cheap and corny element possible: "flying slide" transitions, different and unrelated backgrounds on each slide, even the "typewriter" transition, loudly punctuated with irritating sounds. The title of the PowerPoint is "Randy and Laura Suck and Should Die in a Horrible, Disfiguring Accident Involving Fire, Hydrochloric Acid and Wolverines." A cute picture of Charlotte dressed as an angel pops up and winks.)

Thank you — I know you're clapping for me on the inside. This is me.

(Her yearbook picture appears on the screen.)

And this is Randy

(His yearbook picture appears.)

And Laura.

(As does hers. Suddenly, Randy's and Laura's pictures are scribbled on — beards, glasses, eye-patch, no teeth.)

Oops! Sorry! How did that happen? Let's move on. Here's a picture of me and Randy when we were happy. And one of Laura and me when we were friends. Everybody was happy

(Photo of them all smiling broadly.)

Or were we?

(The same picture, but in this one Charlotte is looking suspiciously at Randy and Laura. The picture changes again. Now Charlotte is looking out toward the audience, shocked, as Randy and Laura kiss in a disgusting manner.)

Not really. Because how can everyone be happy when two of the people are big liars? When they cheat and break your heart to fulfill disgusting, animalistic needs, allowing their hormones to overrule their hearts and minds! Filling the air with noxious falsehoods that scream in the voice of demons borne from the fall of man and the sins of a billion lost souls!! As they look you in the face and lie, equivocate and tear you apart, sneaking off to make the beast with two backs! I'm sorry. Sorry. Carried away a little bit there.

(She claps. A ninja, wearing a bow tie, brings her a glass of water and a facecloth. She drinks and blots. Each of the following statements is accompanied by a photo, often badly photo-shopped.)

Where were you when I was sitting by myself on Friday night? In the park, making out in public. Where were you last winter when I had the measles? Skiing in Aspen. Where were you every Sunday when I was in church, praying that you'd get a job, or that your parents would find a way to work it out? Oh, that's right—you were in Paris together. And where were you when my mother DIED?

(Luke pokes his head in.)

LUKE: Uh, Charlotte? Your mom's still alive

(He exits.)

CHARLOTTE: Shh! You're ruining it! Ehem. And where were you when my MOTHER DIED?

(Picture of JFK's funeral with Charlotte replacing Jackie.)

Oh, right—you were climbing Mount Everest

(Picture of completely proportionally wrong Randy and Laura cut out of two separate semi-formal pictures. Charlotte has drawn in stick-figure hands.)

So what I really want to know is this: *(Her false bravado crumbles:)* Why did you two have to break my heart? *(She cries:)* Why? What did I ever do to you that made you do this to me?

(She collapses in a chair and waves her hand weakly. Two Ninjas enter and unbind and ungag Randy and Laura.)

RANDY: Oh please, oh please! I'm so sorry! Forgive me! I'm worthless! A toad!

LAURA: Mea culpa, mea culpa! I don't deserve your friendship. I'm a worm! I eat dirt!

RANDY: My love, I beg you, if you can find it in your heart to forgive us, I'll give you everything!

CHARLOTTE: *(Pulling herself together:)* Everything?

RANDY: Anything and everything, my love!

CHARLOTTE: Hmm...well if you put it that way...then get the hell out of my life you swine! You don't deserve someone like me!

(She laughs at their misfortune as they crawl away, wailing and gnashing their teeth. She lies down across three chairs, content and tired, humming to herself.)

GEORGE: Hey, Lotte. How's it going?

(George is wearing a scuba mask, snorkel and fins. He has on a bathing suit and a life preserver with an octopus on it.)

CHARLOTTE: Hiya, Georgie. You just missed it! I totally wrecked Randy and Laura. It was great!

GEORGE: Sorry I missed it. I gotta go. Your alarm's about to go off.

CHARLOTTE: What?

(An ALARM BUZZES loudly. Charlotte sits up in bed suddenly and looks around.)

Crap.

(Blackout.)

SCENE 7 — JACK & EDDIE

(Wendy enters.)

WENDY: So maybe I came on too strong? But he seemed really into me. He'd wink at me in the hallway! There was a couple of times where I would wave at him in the hall and he didn't see me. That was terrible. But usually he'd smile that smile. And look at me with those green eyes. On the lunch line, he'd sneak behind me and poke me. Or tickle me. Once he reached behind me and started tickling me so I whipped around quickly and whacked him in the face. He got a bloody nose. It started coming out of his mouth. That was gross. It was worse than the time that Eddie... *(Laughs:)* Oh Eddie. The time he ran into the door... But, I mean, Jack's body language said everything! Once he tackled me to the floor. If that doesn't show affection, I don't know what does! But then he gets all jealous. I can have other friends. I can have friends who are guys. I am capable of having many different variations of friendship. So all of a sudden Jack doesn't want anything to do with me. Perfect. I've tried talking to Eddie about it but he's acting weird too. He keeps asking me if I need a new mirror. My mirror isn't broken... So you know what, I don't care. Whatever Jack was doing with the "winking" and the "poking" and the "laughing" and the... *(Sighs:)* smiling—it doesn't matter. It's meaningless. They do one thing and think another. It never, ever matches. I give up.

(She moves downstage.)

SCENE 8—FLIRTING MONTAGE

(MUSIC plays as Laura, Roxanne, Charlotte, Luke, Randy, George and Eddie join Wendy downstage.)

GEORGE: When it comes to flirting, I can be pretty dense. Then, if I think the girl likes me, I get a little...overzealous.

LAURA: I've seen George flirt. He does this half-smile thing. Makes him look like he's...not quite right in the head.

ROXANNE: I tend to misunderstand a lot of non-verbal cues. I get confused and think that people's insincere feelings are sincere. Consequently, I end up disregarding any social cues from any guy that might actually like me because I'm scared to like them back.

GEORGE: One time we were at this party and some guy brought his cousin from Ohio. The poor guy had Tourette's and he was nervous so he was pretty twitchy all night. Roxanne thought he was coming on to her and spent that whole night trying to dance with him. You should see the video of that!

RANDY: I drop the "cutie" line or compliment a girl's shoes — gets 'em every time. When a girl flirts with me, obviously they find me attractive and that's cool. I can tell by how they look at me. Girls are always touching me at parties.

ROXANNE: You should see Randy at a party. I'm surprised no one's had him arrested for sexual harassment yet. Little red lights start blinking all over the New Jersey Sex Offender registry in the vicinity of the party. It's so gross. "Hey, Cutie."

LUKE: I'm not a physical flirter, per se. A lot of guys like to get all "handsy" with a girl, but I think that's coming on too strong. I'm told I have a way with words.

ROXANNE: You certainly do, honey!

RANDY: "Cough" disgusting "cough" keep it at home, Mom and Dad!

ROXANNE: Shut it, perv!

CHARLOTTE: I try to do silly stuff, like steal a guy's hat and wear it all night at the party. I know he likes me if he keeps trying to get it back all night. The chase is on!

LAURA: Umm...remember the time you took Shawn Carter's hat and got lice?

CHARLOTTE: Not necessary to bring that up, thank you very much! I stand by the hat trick.

EDDIE: Hat trick! That's funny! Get it? Like in hockey? Three goals is a...okay. Forget it.

WENDY: I usually use the same strategy I've had since kindergarten. I tease and make fun of the person I like.

CHARLOTTE: That works well until you tease a guy for coming all dressed up in a suit to a party and ask him if he thought he was coming to a funeral.

WENDY: I didn't know his grandfather died that day! Who goes right from a funeral to a party?

EDDIE: My flirting attempts usually crash and burn. But that turns out to be a good thing because girls think it's cute when you haven't got a smooth bone in your body. Some guys think it's cool to tackle a girl to the ground to show affection. I'd never do that.

RANDY: Correction: he'd never do that <u>anymore</u>. Because the last time he tried, the girl moved out of the way at the last second and he fell down a flight of stairs on my deck. He had a concussion and missed 2 days of school.

LAURA: Ugh. When I'm not into someone and they flirt with me? Worst feeling ever. I'm usually thinking "Uhh...Okay, you can stop now! How can I get out of this? Please, God—make him stop. Let him fall down this flight of stairs and get a concussion or something!"

EDDIE: Wait a minute! You moved on <u>purpose</u>?!

LAURA: Duh.

(Everyone laughs and exits except Randy and Roxanne who stay behind.)

SCENE 9—ADVICE

(Randy and Roxanne move downstage. They dangle their feet off the edge of the stage. They are not wearing shoes.)

ROXANNE: This is where Luke and I come all the time. Our special spot. He asked me out here. It's so tranquil. You'd never know there was a whole town on the other side of that embankment.

RANDY: It's really nice.

ROXANNE: Although one time some idiot kicked a soccer ball down here and beaned me in the back of the head. I almost fell in.

RANDY: *(Preoccupied:)* Oh yeah—it's really nice.

ROXANNE: Randall. Why did you want to talk to me?

RANDY: Roxanne—I really screwed up. You're going to hate me when I tell you this.

ROXANNE: That you cheated on your girlfriend with her best friend, the girl your best friend is still hopelessly in love with even though he has a better chance of winning American Idol by burping the alphabet?

RANDY: Okay. Just listen. That's all I want. Someone to listen for just a minute without judging me.

ROXANNE: I can do that.

RANDY: *(Drawing a deep breath:)* I've never screwed up like this in my life. I lost my girlfriend and my best friend and her best friend all at once because I'm selfish. But it's not like I went and did this on purpose. I hurt three people. Four, if anyone is willing to include me in the equation, which I doubt. I hurt them deeply. But I also love all of them. I know that doesn't make any of what I did right. I'm not looking for anyone to exonerate me. I'm really trying to take responsibility for it.

ROXANNE: So what do you want, then?

RANDY: I want Charlotte back. I've always loved her. I'm just stupid and self-centered and I didn't realize what I had. I'm not even sure how it started. I guess after a while, I started to feel like I was the only one in the relationship. You know, Charlotte sort of...buries her feelings a lot. It's just the way she was raised—they're not a demonstrative family. So I guess I felt...neglected. It sounds so stupid to say now. But that's how I felt at the time. And it wasn't like I was pursuing Laura or she was chasing me. We were all friends. We liked each other. One day she was showing me this painting she was working on. I asked her what it was called and she said that it was so stupid and she didn't know why, but the only thing that came to her mind while she was working on it was me. It was all these swirls of red and gold and orange—like a sky on fire. No one ever named a painting for me before. It was...well, now it just seems stupid. A stupid accident that I couldn't say no to. She made me feel loved when I didn't feel lovable. I'm sorry. I sound so...

ROXANNE: Superficial?

RANDY: Yeah.

ROXANNE: Not really

RANDY: Thanks.

ROXANNE: I'm not sure it was entirely a compliment, but if it makes you feel better, go with it. Why did you come to me with this?

RANDY: I came to you because, well...because you have the only really good relationship I know.

ROXANNE: What?

RANDY: You and Luke—you're perfect together.

ROXANNE: Oh, we're not perfect.

RANDY: You're so good for each other. You give each other space, never take things out on each other. So I thought you'd know what to do. What's wrong?

ROXANNE: We're not perfect. Wow. Okay. I didn't expect this. Not today and not with you. But I always say when God gives you an opportunity, you've gotta seize it. Life lived in fear and all. I'm going to break up with Luke.

RANDY: What?

ROXANNE: I can't keep this relationship up when I go away next year. I love him. But not in the "let's get married" way. He's so special to me. The last thing I want to do is break his heart. But don't I have the right to a life too? I want to start college new. Fresh. I don't want to have to give Fordham half my time and Luke the other half. They both deserve all of me. I deserve all of me. I think.

RANDY: Wow. Didn't expect to hear that.

ROXANNE: See? And you thought you were the only one doing rotten things to the people you love.

RANDY: It's not rotten.

ROXANNE: It is. I'm going to destroy someone I love because I'm selfish.

RANDY: No—what I did was selfish. What you're doing is just...life. Growing up. Moving on. Sometimes people come in and out of our lives and we can't always make them stay.

ROXANNE: Wow. Now it's my turn. That may have been the best thing I've ever heard you say.

RANDY: So what are you going to do?

ROXANNE: I don't know. Break up still, I think. Feel like complete and utter crap about it for a long time. Try to avoid saying "we can still be friends".

RANDY: Yeah—that's a killer line. I'm not sure who it's supposed to make feel better.

ROXANNE: What are you going to do?

RANDY: What do you think?

ROXANNE: I think that the only thing you can do is say you were wrong and ask for forgiveness and wait. I'm always surprised how that's the last thing anyone ever thinks of doing.

RANDY: Well, it's really hard.

ROXANNE: You screwed up. Bad.

RANDY: Yeah, I know.

ROXANNE: *(Standing:)* Well, as much as I've enjoyed our talk...

RANDY: Good luck.

ROXANNE: You too. Watch out for the soccer balls.

(Roxanne exits. Randy sits, lost in thought. Blackout.)

TRANSITION 4

(A video appears on screen. It is a montage with music of Eddie, Wendy and Jack: Eddie teaches Wendy how to drive; she runs over a cone. Wendy waves at Jack down the hall but he doesn't see her; Jack is surrounded by adoring girls; Eddie and Wendy are at a soccer game; Eddie and Wendy are laying on the grass — Jack comes over and Wendy goes with him. Eddie watches them go.)

SCENE 10 — LAURA & GEORGE

(George enters stage right. Laura enters stage left. They both look out.)

LAURA: He brought me to this spot.

GEORGE: It was our spot.

LAURA: It's where he told me that he loved me

GEORGE: Where I told her that I loved her.

LAURA: He held me there.

GEORGE: She held me there.

LAURA: He made me feel so right.

GEORGE: It was just us.

LAURA: Just us.

GEORGE: She took it away.

LAURA: I took it all away.

GEORGE: I still love Laura.

LAURA: I couldn't love him anymore.

GEORGE: She likes Randy now.

LAURA: I thought I loved Randy.

GEORGE: She was so cruel.

LAURA: I was unnecessarily cruel.

GEORGE: She'll never know how I feel.

LAURA: I finally know how he feels.

GEORGE: It can't happen.

LAURA: I wish it never happened.

GEORGE: This spot is where it started.

LAURA: And this spot is where it ended.

(Blackout.)

SCENE 11 – PACKING & MENDING

(Roxanne is packing her bags at stage right. Clothes are everywhere. She looks distraught. Luke enters. He bends down and helps her. They pack in silence for a few moments.)

LUKE: I always liked this shirt.

ROXANNE: I wore it on our first date.

LUKE: I know.

(Silence again.)

You're bringing a lot.

ROXANNE: I know. It's like trying to cram my whole life into a couple suitcases.

LUKE: *(Pause.)* Must be difficult.

ROXANNE: It is.

LUKE: What time do you leave?

ROXANNE: Soon.

LUKE: Too soon.

ROXANNE: How did your audition go?

LUKE: Do we have time to watch a movie once more before you go?

ROXANNE: Luke...

LUKE: I got the lead.

ROXANNE: You're going to be great.

LUKE: I don't know about that.

ROXANNE: You're going to be great.

(The scene freezes. Charlotte is sitting at a table. Randy enters and joins her.)

RANDY: I'm here.

CHARLOTTE: I wasn't waiting for you. I'm done waiting for you.

RANDY: Please. Charlotte. I'm here. For real this time.

CHARLOTTE: And you expect me to believe you?

RANDY: Yes.

CHARLOTTE: What? So you can run off with my best friend again? So you can take everything we had and just throw it away? Like it meant nothing! So you can forget about everything we shared? Just forget about all the things that meant so much to me. ... I thought they meant so much to you too.

RANDY: They do.

CHARLOTTE: How can you sit there and expect me to buy that!? You betrayed my trust, Randy.

RANDY: I know, I know. It got out of hand. It's over. It's done.

CHARLOTTE: You can't just erase something like that.

RANDY: Just give me a second chance. We're worth it.

CHARLOTTE: Why wasn't I good enough for you, Randy? Why wasn't I enough?

RANDY: It's not you! It's not you!... It was me. I made the mistake.

CHARLOTTE: I just don't think I can do this again...

(The scene freezes. Luke and Roxanne continue packing. Luke picks up a stuffed panda bear.)

LUKE: Remember when I won this for you at the St. John Vianney Fair?

ROXANNE: *(Smiling:)* Oh yeah. You tried so hard to knock those cats down. It only took you thirty tries.

LUKE: I really wanted to win you something.

(Roxanne takes the panda from him and squeezes it.)

ROXANNE: Look, Luke...

LUKE: So tell me about the classes you're going to take?

ROXANNE: We don't have time.

LUKE: You can tell me while we pack.

ROXANNE: We'll be done soon.

LUKE: Too soon.

ROXANNE: We have to talk about this. It isn't easy. I—

LUKE: No, Roxi, please. You don't have to do this-

ROXANNE: Luke. You know I love you.

LUKE: Then why are you crying?

ROXANNE: I just can't—do this. We can't do this.

LUKE: Yes. Yes we can. We'll make it work. We're worth it. Aren't we?

(The scene freezes. Randy and Charlotte are at their table.)

RANDY: I can't imagine being without you.

CHARLOTTE: You imagined it just fine when you were with Laura.

RANDY: I was selfish. I didn't know what I was doing.

CHARLOTTE: You knew exactly what you were doing.

RANDY: It meant nothing!

CHARLOTTE: And while it was going on, I meant nothing too, didn't I?

RANDY: I'm so sorry. I don't know how many times I can say that for you to believe me.

CHARLOTTE: I just want you to leave me alone.

RANDY: People make mistakes and screw up, and don't know what they want right away! I just—I just needed a chance to grow up, you know?

CHARLOTTE: Grow up with somebody else's heart.

RANDY: Yours is the only heart worth growing up on.

CHARLOTTE: Another one of your stupid lines.

RANDY: Please forgive me. Give me one more chance.

CHARLOTTE: Something has broken.

RANDY: Just listen.

CHARLOTTE: It won't work this time...

(Charlotte turns away. Randy takes out his guitar and plays her favorite song. The scene freezes but Randy continues to play during Luke and Roxanne's scene.)

ROXANNE: I don't want to hold you back. I don't want you to be hung up on me.

LUKE: But everything was perfect. Everything is perfect.

ROXANNE: It won't be good for us. We won't be able to keep it up.

LUKE: You're giving up!

ROXANNE: There's no other way.

LUKE: We can make it work.

ROXANNE: Please. Just let me go.

LUKE: I can't.

ROXANNE: I'm sorry. I have to go.

LUKE: Please don't.

ROXANNE: I have to. It's time.

(Luke picks up a DVD and hands it to Roxanne.)

LUKE: Don't forget *Casablanca*.

ROXANNE: I'll never forget *Casablanca*.

(She leaves. Luke watches her go. The scene freezes. Randy continues to play. After a while, Charlotte gives in and turns to him.)

CHARLOTTE: You really hurt me.

RANDY: I know.

CHARLOTTE: Do you have any idea what that feels like?

RANDY: Please forgive me.

CHARLOTTE: You're playing our song.

RANDY: I can stop.

CHARLOTTE: I don't want you to stop.

(They kiss as Randy plays on. Blackout.)

SCENE 12—CONFIDENCE

(Randy, Wendy, Luke, Roxanne, George, Charlotte and Laura are sitting in class in various stages of sleep. Eddie's desk is conspicuously empty. The teacher drones on until the sound becomes a hum and then fades away.)

TEACHER (V.O.): Que bonito vestido. Puedo probamelo?

(Randy snores and Charlotte giggles a little. Eddie enters carrying a large CD player. He sets it down.)

EDDIE: Mr. Smith, I— *(He listens to the teacher for a moment and sighs:)* Señor Smith, lamento interrumpir su clase, pero tengo algo muy importante que decir.

(The class is awake and paying attention.)

Wendy. This is for you.

(Eddie pushes a button on the CD player. Nothing happens. He reaches into his bag and takes out a large orange extension cord, plugs the CD player into it and plugs the cord into the outlet offstage.)

Wendy. This is for you.

(He pushes a button on the CD player and nothing happens again. He clears his throat awkwardly and sings a capella to "I Have Confidence" from The Sound of Music.*)*

WHAT WILL MY DAY BE LIKE? I WONDER.
WHAT WILL YOUR FUTURE BE? I WONDER.
IT WOULD BE SO EXCITING IF THIS SONG WOULD SET YOU FREE
MY HEART WOULD BE WILDLY REJOICING
BUT I'M SOMEONE YOU NEVER SEE.

I'VE ALWAYS WANTED TO TELL YOU
NEVER EXPECT TO BE TONGUE-TIED
AND NOW THAT MOMENT'S UPON US
SO WHY AM I FEELING SHY (-D)?

SINGING A SONG IN FRONT OF ALL YOUR FRIENDS—
WHAT'S SO FEARSOME ABOUT THAT?

NOW I KNOW THAT YOU HAVE RESERVATIONS
ABOUT HOW FRIENDS CAN NEVER DATE
BUT HERE I AM STANDING BEFORE YOU
ALLOW ME TO ELUCIDATE

(Spoken.)

I looked that up

I KNOW THAT YOU LOVE SOUND OF MUSIC
AND I HOPE THAT MARIA HELPS ME
TO SHOW YOU I'M WORTH IT
I WROTE YOU THIS SONG
SO YOU SEE

THAT I'D DO ANYTHING YOU WANT TO
PLAY "GUESS WHO" UNTIL I DROP
GIVE UP SHAMPOO, WASH MY HAIR WITH SODA POP

BUT I'LL MAKE YOU SEE THAT THERE'S SO MUCH MORE
TO ME

I COULDN'T WRITE A RAP SONG
YOU COULDN'T DRIVE A CAR
BUT, AND I SWEAR BY MILTON BRADLEY,
YOU WILL FIND THINGS IN ME, SURPRISING

ONCE I WAS AN UGLY CHICKEN
WE WERE BEST FRIENDS, I CONCEDE
I AM PRAYING THAT I WILL BE WHAT YOU NEED
AND YOU WILL AGREE THAT THERE'S SO MUCH MORE
TO ME

WHEN YOU CLEAN UP ALL MY NOSEBLEEDS
WHEN YOU WALK UPON YOUR HANDS
WHEN YOU TELL JACK THAT HE'S NOT SO MUCH TO
SEE
YOU'LL HAVE TO AGREE THAT THERE'S SO MUCH
MORE TO ME

LOVE CAN'T BE FOUND IN POEMS
LOVE CAN'T BE FOUND IN HAIR
LOVE LIES IN AWKWARD CHICKEN RAP SONGS
GIVE ME YOUR HAND—GOD, PLEASE! I'M DYING!

I WOULD TAKE YOU TO A GARDEN
WRITE YOUR NAME UP IN THE SKY
ALL I WANT IS YOU TO LET ME BE YOUR GUY

   (Spoken.)

Awkward. I hate myself.

ALL I WANT IS YOU TO LET ME BE YOUR GUY
AND I'LL MAKE YOU SEE THERE IS SO MUCH MORE TO
ME!

   (A beat.)

(With great abandon:) Wendy McGann — will you go out with me!?

WENDY: Yes! I totally will!

(She runs to him and jumps into his arms. He picks her up and spins her around and then puts her gently on the ground. He kisses her and the room explodes in applause. Blackout. End of play.)

The Authors Speak

What inspired you to write this play?
We had been working with the same group of actors for three
or four years—they were exceptional young men and women,
giving, dedicated and inspiring. John and I had simultaneous
ideas we had been thinking about privately. When John said,
"What do you think about writing a play this summer and
collaborating" with these actors, I immediately blurted out "I'd
been thinking about doing a play that focused on high school
relationships and took them as seriously as they really are!"

Was the structure of the play influenced by any other work?
The play is structured as a series of interwoven vignettes that
was influenced by (insert playwright) and novels such as
Sandra Cisneros's *The House on Mango Street*. The play's comic
sensibility and use of fantastical and metaphysical techniques
can be linked to many works by Woody Allen.

**Have you dealt with the same theme in other works that you
have written?**
The theme of high school relationships was also explored in
our follow-up piece *Something About Friendship*.

**What writers have had the most profound effect on your
style?**
Woody Allen, Samuel Beckett. Caryl Churchill, Paul Thomas
Anderson, Michael Arndt.

What do you hope to achieve with this work?
Here's what no adult ever admits: high school relationships
are usually difficult and painful. Most adults scoff at or
minimize the importance of these nascent connections as a
defense mechanism, unable or unwilling to admit how crucial
these moments were. It's these embarrassing, awkward,
difficult, scary and wonderful relationships that we wanted to
explore—and to treat them with the reverence they deserve.

What are the most common mistakes that occur in productions of your work?
Our hope with this work is that the audience sees each of these characters as real teenagers. If the actors portray them so they are believable and relatable to the audience, they have succeeded. There are no "mistakes" as long as the director has a clear vision because it is a joy to see their interpretation come alive on stage.

How did you research the subject?
Discovering the ideas for this show resulted in a collaborative process between us as playwrights and twelve high school juniors and seniors. We discussed ideas such as "what was your first kiss like?" and "how do you flirt?" and listened to stories about relationships gone wrong, how it feels to go away to college and leave someone behind, and what students daydream about in class. From there, the characters grew, their relationships coalesced and the work came to life.

Do any films/videos exist of prior productions of this play?
Yes. We have DVDs of our original production at Union Catholic High School. There is also a DVD of a production performed at the Bordentown Performing Arts Center.

Shakespeare gave advice to the players in *Hamlet*; if you could give advice to your cast what would it be?
Speak the speech, we pray you, as we pronounced it to you, trippingly on the tongue. But be real, be yourself, and follow the heart's truth of the words.

How was the first production different from the vision that you created in your mind?
We directed and produced the first four productions of the play, so our vision simply refined itself slightly as we went along. However, we had the opportunity to see the play performed by two other high schools and it is the most

exhilarating feeling to watch is and see each actor and director's individual fingerprints on each character. We love watching to see what each production does differently and the moments they find that are exactly the same as we directed them. The best part about the structure and intent our writing is that it not only allows but encourages new and different interpretations of the same ideas. The actors and directors can follow the heart's truth of the script and arrive at very different conclusions and interpretations.

About the Authors

John Rotondo is a playwright, screenwriter, director and producer. He is the Co-Founder and Co-Artistic Director of Fourteen Out of Ten Productions, a production company dedicated to creating a collaborative theatrical environment between students and professionals. His work for the stage includes: *Love (Awkwardly)*, which won the audience favorite award at Manhattan Theatre Source (New York, NY), *Storage, Something About Friendship, The House She Built, Write for Me* and *The Boarding House.* John graduated from the Goldberg Department of Dramatic Writing in NYU's Tisch School of the Arts. He was a finalist for the Hanger Theatre's Playwriting Lab Residency and serves as the director of fall productions for the Union Catholic Performing Arts Company. His website is www.14outof10.org.

Maryann Carolan is a playwright, screenwriter, designer and teacher. She is the Co-Founder and Co-Artistic Director of Fourteen out of Ten Productions, whose mission is to combine the vitality of students with the experience of professionals in a collaborative theatrical environment. Her work for the stage includes: *Love (Awkwardly)* (Winner — Audience Favorite Award at Manhattan Theatre Source & Nominated for 6 MSU

Theatre Night Awards), ***Storage, Something About Friendship, Teacher of the Year,*** and ***The Boarding House.*** Maryann received a Writing & Philosophy Fellowship from the University of St. Andrews, Scotland and was a finalist in the Hanger Theatre's Playwriting Lab Residency. She also serves as Director of the Union Catholic Performing Arts Company in Scotch Plains, NJ. Her website is www.14outof10.org.

About YouthPLAYS

YouthPLAYS (www.youthplays.com) is a publisher of award-winning professional dramatists and talented new discoveries, each with an original theatrical voice, and all dedicated to expanding the vocabulary of theatre for young actors and audiences. On our website you'll find one-act and full-length plays and musicals for teen and pre-teen (and even college) actors, as well as duets and monologues for competition. Many of our authors' works have been widely produced at high schools and middle schools, youth theatres and other TYA companies, both amateur and professional, as well as at elementary schools, camps, churches and other institutions serving young audiences and/or actors worldwide. Most are intended for performance by young people, while some are intended for adult actors performing for young audiences.

YouthPLAYS was co-founded by professional playwrights Jonathan Dorf and Ed Shockley. It began merely as an additional outlet to market their own works, which included a substantial body of award-winning published and unpublished plays and musicals. Those interested in their published plays were directed to the respective publishers' websites, and unpublished plays were made available in electronic form. But when they saw the desperate need for material for young actors and audiences—coupled with their experience that numerous quality plays for young people weren't finding a home—they made the decision to represent the work of other playwrights as well. Dozens and dozens of authors are now members of the YouthPLAYS family, with scripts available both electronically and in traditional acting editions. We continue to grow as we look for exciting and challenging plays and musicals for young actors and audiences.

About ProduceaPlay.com

Let's put up a play! Great idea! But producing a play takes time, energy and knowledge. While finding the necessary time and energy is up to you, ProduceaPlay.com is a website designed to assist you with that third element: knowledge.

Created by YouthPLAYS' co-founders, Jonathan Dorf and Ed Shockley, ProduceaPlay.com serves as a resource for producers at all levels as it addresses the many facets of production. As Dorf and Shockley speak from their years of experience (as playwrights, producers, directors and more), they are joined by a group of award-winning theatre professionals and experienced teachers from the world of academic theatre, all making their expertise available for free in the hope of helping this and future generations of producers, whether it's at the school or university level, or in community or professional theatres.

The site is organized into a series of major topics, each of which has its own page that delves into the subject in detail, offering suggestions and links for further information. For example, Publicity covers everything from Publicizing Auditions to How to Use Social Media to Posters to whether it's worth hiring a publicist. Casting details Where to Find the Actors, How to Evaluate a Resume, Callbacks and even Dealing with Problem Actors. You'll find guidance on your Production Timeline, The Theater Space, Picking a Play, Budget, Contracts, Rehearsing the Play, The Program, House Management, Backstage, and many other important subjects.

The site is constantly under construction, so visit often for the latest insights on play producing, and let it help make your play production dreams a reality.

More from YouthPLAYS

Uncertainty Theory by Maura Campbell
Drama with music. 40-50 minutes. 6-10+ females, 5-10+ males (11-30 performers possible).

High school graduation day. Senior girls and boys get into their gowns as they prepare for their last day together. Suddenly, there is an ambulance in the parking lot and a report that one of the students may have died. First seen through the eyes of the graduating girls, then through the eyes of the graduating boys, *Uncertainty Theory* celebrates the power of lifelong friendships, as it contemplates alternate universes and how the future can be altered in a single moment.

Enemy|Flint by Diana Burbano
Drama. 70-80 minutes. 5-17+ females, 3-15+ males (10-20+ performers possible).

Thia Stockmann, a bright young medical student, has discovered her hometown's water supply has been poisoned. Her data, her personality and her determination offend first her family, then the town council, then the community. As her friends and allies buckle under the pressure, Thia refuses to run from doing what is right, even if that means becoming "an enemy of the people."

Slow by Keegon Schuett
Drama. 45-55 minutes. 3 females, 1 male, 1 either.

Lizzy Slominski is better known to her classmates as "Camera Girl," because she's always hiding behind her digital camera snapping photos of strangers. Her days as a loner end when a mysterious new boy appears at the bus stop. Will she be able to put down her camera and connect, or is she doomed to a life of observing through the lens?

Harry's Hotter at Twilight by Jonathan Dorf
Comedy. 90-100 minutes. 7-25+ females, 5-25+ males (12-50+ performers possible).

In this crazed mash-up parody of *Harry Potter* and *Twilight*—with cameos crashing in from *Lord of the Rings*, *Star Wars*, *Alice in Wonderland* and many other places—you'll encounter deli-owning vegetarians, invisible rabbits, magical carrot weapons, random lunatics, soothing offstage voices, evil gourmets and much more, as everyone's favorite wizards, vampires and werewolves battle to save miserable, gloomy Spork—and indeed the world—from certain destruction.

Great Expectations by Rocco P. Natale
Drama. 75-90 minutes. 1-7 females, 1-5 males (4-8 performers possible).

In this new adaptation of Charles Dickens' classic novel, a young orphan boy named Pip is made rich by a mysterious benefactor who believes in Pip's "great expectations." Pip imagines the eccentric Miss Havisham has made his fortune, but all is not as it appears. Can Pip solve the mystery of his own circumstances and win the affections of the beautiful Estella? Love triumphs in this story of the human heart.

Carolina Dive by Neeley Gossett
Drama. 30-35 minutes. 5-10 females, 2-4 males (7-12 performers possible, plus extras).

Jenna is a teenager living in a place known only for race cars and beauty pageants. When her friends discover an old bridge, diving off it becomes her obsession. Her strange, solitary nighttime practices make her an outcast, but the possibility of diving for a college team gives her a way to escape the small town. But when a dive damages her inner ear and she can no longer keep her balance, are her future plans in jeopardy?

Xtigone by Nambi E. Kelley
Drama. 90-100 minutes. 5-15+ females, 4-15+ males (9-30+ performers possible).

Chicago. Present day. Xtigone's brothers have been killed in drive-by shootings by each other's rival gang. Her powerful uncle calls for the bodies to be buried instead of uncovering the violence in the city streets. In this re-imagining of Sophocles' *Antigone* that uses poetry, dance and dialogue that speak with an urban voice, will Xtigone go against his edict and risk death in her quest for her community's truth?

Les Examables by Don Zolidis
Comedy. 100-110 minutes. 8-28 females, 5-25 males (15-40+ performers possible).

Tired of too much standardized testing in her high school, high achiever Anna Ullman stages a protest and finds herself crowned the new principal. But ultimate power comes with its own problems (especially after death threats from the all-powerful State Board of Ed), and soon Anna descends into madness, imposing even more standardized testing. It's up to her former best friend, Lola, to bring down this new tyrant. Soon Lola is manning the barricades and singing triumphantly awesome songs in this insane satire based on the mega-musical *Les Misérables*.

How the Elephant Got His Trunk by Cary Nothnagel
Comedy. 25-35 minutes. 7-17 females, 5-12 males (8-24 performers possible).

When Elton's questions become too much for his family and neighbors, the young elephant sets out to find his own answers. But it's said that curiosity killed the cat, and it may not be healthy for elephants either. Will Elton's insatiable inquisitiveness make him wiser, or will it make him dinner?

Made in the USA
Middletown, DE
17 July 2022

69037300R00050